GCSE and Standard Grade

DESIGN & COMMUNICATION

RICHARD TUFNELL

First published in 1989 by Hutchinson Education
(ISBN 0–09–173213–1)

Reprinted in 1994 by:
Stanley Thornes (Publishers) Ltd
Ellenborough House
Wellington Street
CHELTENHAM GL50 1YD
England

A catalogue record of this book is available from the British Library.

ISBN 0–7487–1078–7

Designed by Ron Kamen
Text set by Microset Graphics, Basingstoke
Printed and bound by Dah Hua Printing Press, Hong Kong

Acknowledgements

I would like to thank the following companies and organizations for the help they have given me in the preparation of this book:
  Agfa-Gaevert, Beecham, The British Standards Institute, The Body Shop, Cadbury Schweppes, The Design Council, Evode Ltd, Ford UK Ltd, Halco Ltd, Indesit, Isuzu, Klemetric Displays Ltd, Letraset UK, London Transport, National Motor Museum, National Westminster Bank, Nationwide Anglia Building Society, Ordnance Survey, Reckitt and Coleman, and Ross Electronics.

The following design consultancies have been most generous in allowing me to use examples of their work, and I would especially like to thank individuals at these consultancies who have been particularly helpful in answering questions and supplying artwork:
  Sarah Coles and Jon Wealleans at Crighton Design Management Consultants, Norman Hands at Engineering Model Associates, Paul Stead at Fitch & Co, Peter Clark at Keraflo Ltd, John Hurst at Nettle, John Boult at Product First, Philip Gray at Roberts Weaver, and Andy Ewan at The Yellow Pencil. Thanks also to Porsche Design Studio, Richard Rogers & Partners, and Seymour Harris Partnership.

The following examination boards have given permission to reproduce questions from 1988 GCSE examination papers:
  London and East Anglian Examination Board, Midland Examining Group, Northern Examining Association, Northern Ireland Schools Examinations Council, Southern Examining Group, and Welsh Joint Education Committee.

A number of friends have helped in producing illustrations and artwork. I would particularly like to thank:
  Gary Calvert, Bill Dexter, John Farmer, Geoff Pragnell, and Roman Piotrowski.

The book also includes work done by the following teachers, students and pupils:
  Paul Browne, Richard Caby, Janet Campbell, Gillian Coxshall, Rosemary Eley, Tim Ford, Pauline Forster, Barbara Guy, Paul Hossier, Andrew Jones, Hugh Jones, Sally Law, Bill Nicholl, Yogandera Patel, Tony Pennock, Brian Porter, Alan Priestman, Paul Pritchard, Laura Regazzacci, Gillian Rogers, Mike Sadler, Graham Stevens, Loraine Stoker, Philip Swindel, and David Waites.

My apologies to anybody I have omitted from this list.

I am also most grateful for the constant stimulus and motivation I receive from my colleagues and students at Middlesex Polytechnic, and the teachers I come into contact with on in-service courses. All have helped me maintain my interest and enthusiasm for the subject. In particular amongst my colleagues I would wish to thank John Cave and Peter Shipley who are a constant source of ideas and enthusiasm.

Finally, I am especially grateful to my wife, Val. As well as offering considerable advice and criticism and checking the manuscript she has been tolerant and patient, but above all encouraging and enthusiastic, throughout the two years that this project has taken.

Contents

INTRODUCTION

CORE STUDIES

1 ANALYTICAL DRAWING

2 ORTHOGRAPHIC DRAWING

3 TECHNICAL GRAPHICS

4 PICTORIAL AND PRESENTATION DRAWING

Communicating ideas

It is easy to embark on a project without thinking through all the consequences of our chosen course of action. When we attempt to design in our minds we often get something wrong. It is not that we have not considered a problem or imagined an idea but that usually we find it impossible to put all our thoughts together into a solution which takes every factor into account.

Everyone involved in design has at their disposal a range of techniques or tools which will help them record, develop and solve problems. You have already gained some experience in these techniques which enable you to communicate with yourself and with others. No technique or method will solve a problem for you, that will depend on your ability to think both creatively and logically. Design is a complex activity and the best way to improve is by having a go.

Whilst searching for solutions to any brief you may use sketches, diagrams, pictorial views, working drawings, exploded views, cut away views and a variety of different types of models. You will use pencils, pens, markers, specialized drawing equipment such as parallel motions and airbrushes, computers and so on. You will work with a wide range of materials — layout, cartridge and bleedproof paper, card, plastics and other modelling materials. It is a pretty complex subject but remember — all these things are there to help you do the job in hand, they are not an end in themselves. How, when and why to use each of these skills and media in reaching solutions is what this subject is all about.

If you have recently moved on to this book from *Introducing Design and Communication* you will remember that one of the case studies related to the design of the Durabeam torch. The design story on this page shows how two students tackled a brief to design a torch for the same market. They used the full range of skills and knowledge which this subject requires. But you will only be successful if as well as acquiring skills you develop a curiosity about everything around you, use your initiative and ingenuity, become resourceful and set yourself standards. You may not become a professional designer but you will be a consumer of designers' work. Try to be discriminating — you should learn to make valued judgements about **aesthetic**, **technical**, **economic** and **moral** issues (how do things look, do they work efficiently, are they cost effective and will they be beneficial and useful?).

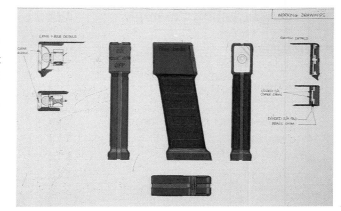

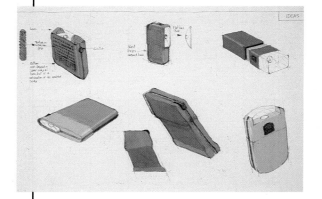

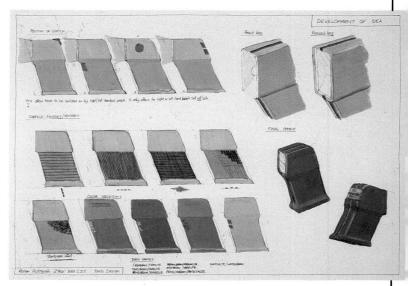

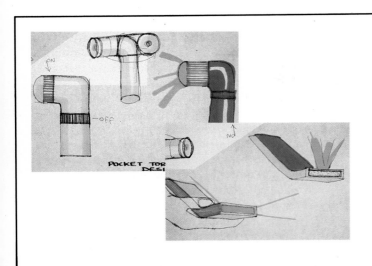

POCKET TORCH
DESIGN

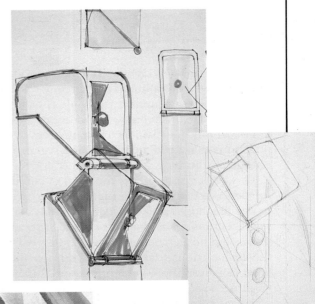

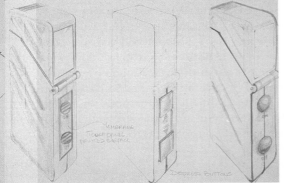

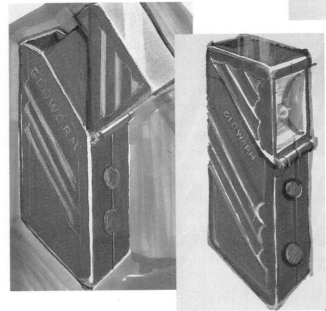

ALTERNATIVE SURFACE TEXTURES

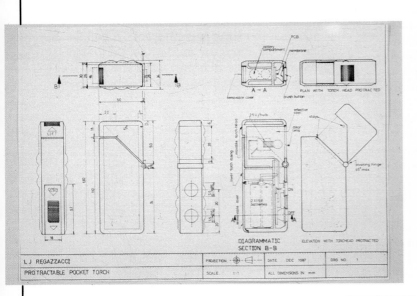

DIAGRAMMATIC
SECTION B-B

L J REGAZZACCI

PROTRACTABLE POCKET TORCH

| PROJECTION | DATE | DEC 1987 | DRG NO. | 1 |
| SCALE | 1:1 | ALL DIMENSIONS IN mm |

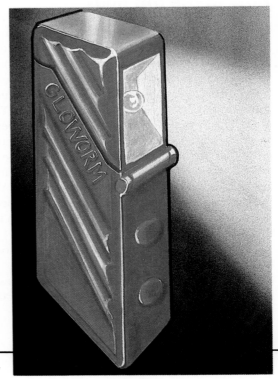

About this book

This book has been designed to help you study for your GCSE examination in design and communication. You have probably chosen this subject because you enjoy it and hope to do well in it. I hope this book will give you answers to all the questions that need answering and will provide ideas and inspiration.

This book builds on the foundation laid down in *Introducing Design and Communication*. Do not start to use this book until you feel confident with the skills, techniques and ways of working recommended in the first book. Neither of these books can replace the advice and guidance which your teacher can offer. However, there are a number of things which you might wish to do independently. There are more activities in this book than you could possibly do during your course, so be selective.

You will be sitting a specific examination set by one of the GCSE boards. This book attempts to cover the elements which are common to all examinations. There may be some aspects which are not necessary for your examination. Conversely, there may be a few things which are not covered which you need to know for your examination. Your teacher will have a copy of the syllabus and he or she will tell you exactly what is required. Make sure you know how you will be examined as well as what you have to know. Success in the examination depends a great deal on your ability to organize and manage the resources and facilities available to you. One of the most important resources is time — you must try to work consistently over the two-year period because your coursework could be worth up to 50 per cent of the final mark.

How to use this book

This book has two sections: *Core studies* and *Specialist studies*. *Core studies* covers a whole variety of skills and techniques which are part of most syllabuses. *Specialist studies* focuses on project work. It gives examples of projects, some by students and some undertaken by professional designers. There are ten units in the book, seven in *Core studies* and three in *Specialist studies*. Although units focus on particular areas, when you come to tackle the activities in each area you will use a much wider range of design and commmunication skills. You will be drawing on your background which has been developing ever since you coloured a picture book or drew in a sandpit.

Look from section to section as you need to. Use the book as a resource to tackle the selected activities. Many of the activities in *Core studies* can be expanded into minor or major projects. If this is the case the activity will be marked*.

The first unit in *Specialist Studies* deals with possible project areas. Design and communication is a wide ranging subject and for convenience it has been divided into four basic areas:

1 Environmental — this is sometimes called spatial design. It includes architecture, interior design, landscape design and exhibition design.
2 Information — all aspects of graphic design, packaging, advertising, corporate identity, instructional graphics and statistical graphics.
3 Technological — the design of control systems, which might be electrical, mechanical, pneumatic or hydraulic.
4 Industrial — the packaging of technological systems, the design of consumer products, ergonomics, making sure that an article will do what it is intended to do efficiently and easily.

In the majority of design situations these areas overlap. The exhibition designer will be involved with the graphics of an exhibition as well as its physical arrangement and the industrial designer will more often than not take a hand in the technology inside a product. This division will help to focus your mind. After each section there are some suggestions as to where to look for design projects, but remember marks are allocated for the recognition of a problem so no specific briefs are given.

Unit 9 covers presentation which is vital to every aspect of this subject and you should refer to it constantly. Communication is about making yourself understood, so the more clearly your ideas and solutions are presented the better chance you stand of being understood!

The final unit gives you the opportunity to have a go at some previous examination questions. They are taken from all the examination boards. They are mainly from specimen papers as there have been very few actual examinations so far. These will give you a good idea of what to expect when it comes to the examination.

This is the point where I could wish you good luck — but you will not need luck if you work sensibly and conscientiously and act on all the advice you will receive. Above all, try and enjoy the subject. It is challenging, interesting and enjoyable. It will teach you a great deal about the modern world in which you live, and by the end of two years you may well have some good ideas about how our environment might be improved!

Thinking about design

Designing is always a challenge, whether it concerns a small elastic powered vehicle or a passenger airliner. The scale of the problem is obviously different, but then so are the resources. The similarity between the two situations is that the designers will attempt to make decisions and predictions about something that as yet does not exist. The success of that something will depend on the designers' creative and practical capabilities.

A designer has to make decisions about the potential of what is being designed without fully knowing how it will work, look or operate. Naturally, designers attempt to solve every problem and view their designs from every angle, but to get everything spot on all the time they would have to be crystal ball gazers rather than designers. Market research, endurance testing and prototype modelling all help to reduce the risk, but as we know, buildings do sometimes fall down, mass produced cars do often get recalled and we often do hear about environmental pollution — all the results of designers not quite getting it right. On a more personal scale, how often do things not work as we anticipated, not last as long as we expected, or not live up to their promotion? Well thankfully not very often, but there is always room for improvement.

The most common feeling on completion of a design project, apart from the feeling of satisfaction, is 'if only I had known what I know now at the start of the project, I could have done it better'. Obviously the more we know the better our chance of producing a competent solution. Always remember, for a designer there is no single right answer. There are better solutions and worse ones, probably even a best at a particular moment in time, but today's best solution will probably not be tomorrow's! As a designer you must understand the present before you can start predicting the future.

How do designers think?

School is often very confusing. The range of subjects that you might tackle in any one day and the different modes of thinking they require demands a flexible mind. **Scientific** thinking is about accurate description leading to an explanation of why and how. In **art** you re-interpret the world through your own imagination and emotions, giving them external form in a range of media. **Mathematical** thought is abstract, often involving symbols in the solving of problems that did not exist before the mathematician established a hypothesis that needed proving. Designers draw on all these methods but still have their own distinctive way of going about things.

Designers must use scientific methods to carry out research and set up experiments to discover the ground rules. Designers must use their intuition when looking for possible answers, running through their data base of knowledge, selecting, adapting, compromising and creating. This ability to explore ideas is often helped by sketches and it involves hunches and gut feelings, needing artistic inspiration. Designers must be mathematically logical — they need to establish specifications, criteria against which to judge their work. Above all, designers need flexible minds, the capacity to adapt to new situations and new possibilities, and the vision to arrange variables into new solutions.

Designing is never easy. Often when a designer starts work on a brief it quickly becomes apparent that the wrong problem is being addressed. For example, queuing at a checkout in a supermarket or a counter in a post office is boring. Problem: how can the boredom be relieved? Answer: play music and videos. This is a poor solution as it creates many more problems. The real problem is, how to shorten or remove the queues, not the boredom! So the problem may change as the project progresses. Designers also have to be decisive, they need to know when to run with an idea, and when the payoff from additional work will not justify the effort. Approaching a problem within the constraints of the given resources is the reality with which a designer must operate.

How do designers work?

Is there a **design method**? There is no simple answer to this question. There are many **models**, or ways of working, which certainly help and guide those with little experience. There is a great deal of common sense in designing, for example, it is obvious that you should find out about the common sizes of paper before designing a portfolio. Many of the models indicate that there are certain stages through which you should progress to find the best solution, but in reality designing is a bit like a game of snakes and ladders. You can be getting quite close to a solution, then suddenly some aspect of the project changes and you feel as though you are back at square one. However, this is not the case — you are now much wiser and can recognize the dead ends which lead nowhere. In contrast, sometimes you can take a giant step forward, an intuitive leap to the eureka solution, the ladder which suddenly advances you quickly towards your goal.

Design method sounds rather restrictive, a bit like a straightjacket, not an approach that will encourage creative solutions. It might be better instead to think in terms of **design strategies**, a range of tactics which can be employed as appropriate. A design will evolve in response to the tactics being used or not being used. Perhaps one of the real skills of a designer is knowing how to approach the search and when to change course and look at the problem from a different angle. It takes a great deal of experience to be a competent designer. You can only be taught so much — there is no substitute for having a go.

There is a great deal to be learnt from case studies showing how others have tackled a brief. You will find a number in this book. The case study on pages 8–13 deals with an everyday product, something to which you might not give a second thought. You might even regard it as a trivial problem, but on the contrary, it is the result of clear, logical and creative thinking.

Product First is a relatively new consultancy, founded by a splinter group from a much larger consultancy. The company is run by three directors. John Boult is responsible for marketing the group, talking to clients and promoting the consultancy's image and profile to potential clients. The two other founding members are Graham Thomson and David Scothron, both industrial designers who had worked for a number of organizations before teaming up with John.

When they were with their previous consultancy, Brand New Industrial Design, they tackled an interesting product for Evode. The case study shows how a successful result was achieved. In another situation with different ingredients the strategies and tactics used might well have been different, as might the solution. Take advice, listen and look, but in the end you are the designer and you will have to take the responsibility for producing your best solution, even if it is an elastic powered vehicle!

Design in action — the Evostick glue dispenser

When a company realizes that it has a gap in its product range, that it can expand the range, or that a product needs updating, one of its options is to call in a design consultancy. Your teacher will play the role of a company by setting you a number of briefs or mini-projects during the first year of your course. In the final year, however, you will probably have to come up with your own brief for your major project. It is unlikely that someone will commission you. Either identifying or being given a brief is the first stage in any design project.

Evode felt many people did not know of the wide range of adhesives available for both simple and more difficult household tasks. In particular, there are now some special glues produced to tackle specific gluing problems. At the initial briefing they stressed the potential market and cost of the product. They wanted the glue dispenser to be as useful in the home as in the office, attractive and modern to look at and safe to carry about in briefcase or handbag.

After several meetings with the clients, a contract would be established. A contract of this type would include, for example, the time scale for the design and its cost. In any brief you undertake always determine your working constraints — the resources at your disposal. This will certainly include how long you have to complete the project, and also other factors, such as the availability of materials and facilities. Getting this wrong and overstretching yourself might result in a poor final result. For consultancies such as Product First, undertaking too much for too little could have very serious consequences, so they have to get it right.

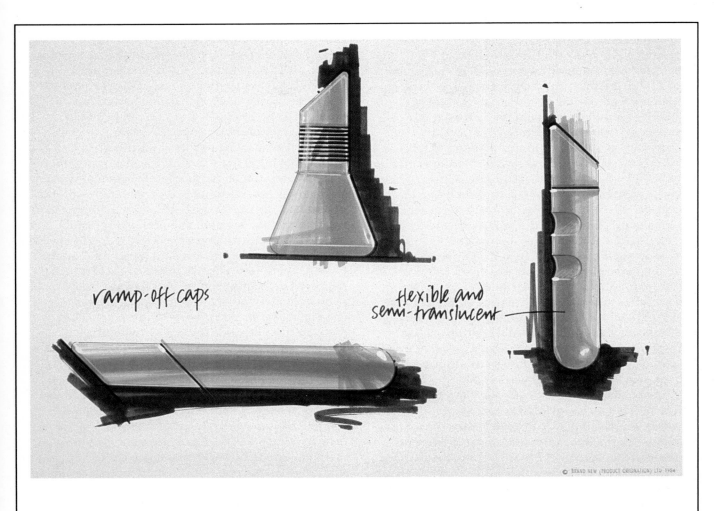

ramp-off caps

flexible and
semi-translucent

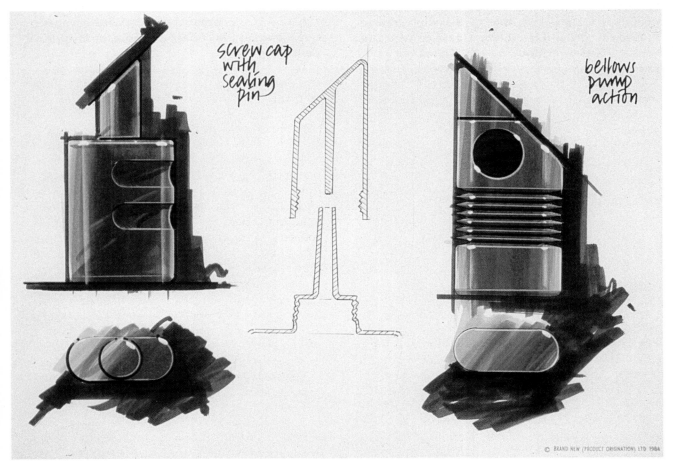

screw cap
with
sealing
pin

bellows
pump
action

The glue dispenser posed both technical and aesthetic problems. The design team started by establishing exactly what the problem was, defining what they thought the client wanted and what were the targets or objectives. You might call this a **specification** or the **design objectives**. It is a statement describing the functions and characteristics your solution should try to meet. When you start to suggest possible answers, they can be tested against this list. It prevents a designer from losing sight of what he or she is really trying to achieve.

Graham Thomson, as the senior designer of the team, looked at the technical problems. As in any situation you can learn a great deal by seeing how others have solved the problem. **Research** is usually essential, although in some situations your own experience and knowledge may be sufficient as a starting point. The type of glue to be used could be dispensed from a tube with a screw top, a glass bottle with a rubber dispenser, an aerosol, or a can with a spatula, but none of these would have met the brief, so a fresh approach was needed.

The challenge was to create a leak-proof reservoir, which could be easily filled during manufacture, and which would allow glue to be dispensed cleanly, as and when required, without the glue drying and blocking the dispenser. A plastic container satisfied the criteria set in the original specification. Blow moulding appeared the obvious choice of production method but injection moulding was chosen as it provided a better mechanical, physical and economic solution to the problem. The key issue appeared to be the seal — after the reservoir was filled with glue, how could it be effectively sealed? This is not a new

problem. Seals of this type exist, but not in a small-scale hand-held object. Established principles had to be understood by the design team and reinterpreted to meet their needs. **Sketches** helped determine possible solutions and allowed their potential to be analysed. The solution had to be simple — no gaskets, O rings or clamping devices, just two parts locking together — but how?

After looking at many possible answers a solution was reached which was simple, efficient and cheap. You can see how the double seal operates — it relies on interlocking ribs in the body of the moulding. You will find that the solution to a problem generally evolves, and gradually becomes refined. It will involve sketches and models to test your ideas and hunches. First ideas are very valuable but can nearly always be improved on by thinking around the brief and approaching it from a different aspect. Always record all your thoughts. You may need to come back to them if things do not work out as you had anticipated.

The technical problem solved, Graham first moved on to the ergonomics of the dispenser, which were closely linked to the visual appearance. The product is hand held. This obviously imposes contraints within which to work. The other important factor not to be forgotten at this stage is the volume of the glue reservoir. Renderings with markers were used to give substance to concepts which could then be tested on the client. Reactions enabled the designers to refine the look and feel of the dispenser and start to make **form models** — solid block models in foam or wood. As this process continued, the detailing became more and more exact until a consensus of approval was reached.

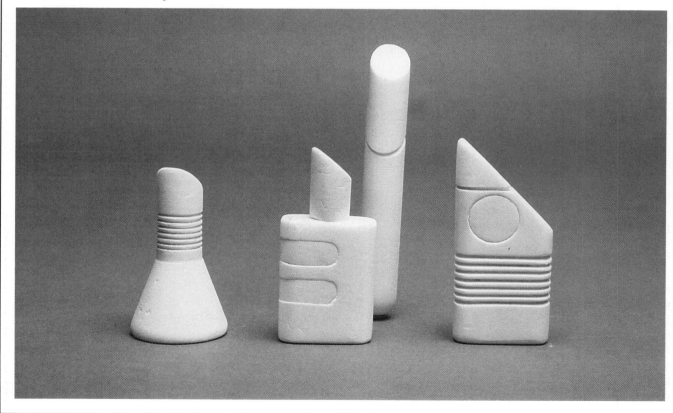

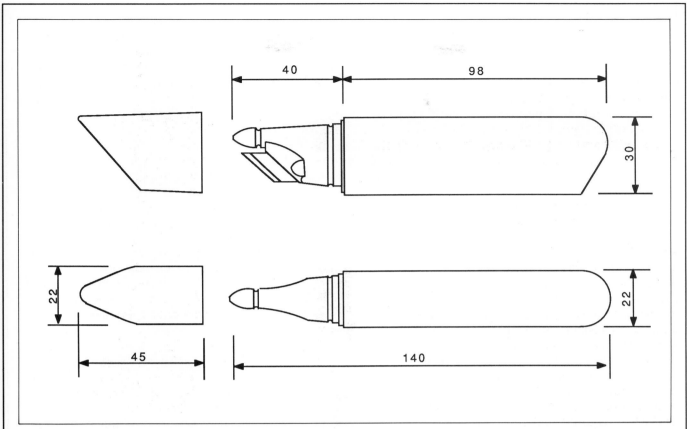

Now possible colours for the containers could be examined. The containers had to use exisiting colours already used by Evode for some glues (for example wood glue is normally packaged in green containers) and also specify new colours that worked well as a range and reflected the glue's use. Colour also has to provide a good backdrop for product information. The best way to test these aspects is on solid models, which can be used for **market research**. Feedback helps the designer get the best solution for the majority of people. When you are designing you will find that every project involves technical and visual problems (**function** and **form**). They are always closely intertwined and can very rarely be dealt with in isolation. Decisions and solutions to one aspect will affect the other. You must learn to handle them simultaneously. Things that function efficiently are usually good to look at and generally the reverse to this is true; however, appearance is a subjective aspect and so is more difficult to judge. Both aspects are equally important.

Once all aspects of the design have been agreed a **prototype model** can be commissioned. This will resemble in every aspect the manufactured product, it will be accurate to the very last detail. To achieve this the designers had to produce detailed **working drawings** of each part and **assembled views** from which the model maker could work. The glue dispenser was prototyped as a working model so that every feature of the design could be evaluated. The client could take the models away and submit them to rigorous tests — at this stage it was still not too late to change aspects of the design. After minor modifications managerial approval was given. The

manufacturing stage had been reached. The designers adjusted the working drawings. The accuracy of the final product and of the tool making operation, which is now using CNC equipment, depend on these drawings. Complex curved moulds, such as the ones that would be required for this product, are made using a spark eroder. The design team are responsible for checking the quality of the mouldings to ensure their specifications are being met.

It is very unlikely that any of the things which you design at school will be more than one-offs. The prototype model will frequently, for you, be the end of the process. On some occasions your final model might not even be that advanced — your solution might be presented in two dimensions. Remember though, it is essential to maintain close communication with the client. Designing is not a self-indulgent occupation, it is about trying to meet real and perceived needs. Evaluation is also a vital tool. The ability to dispassionately assess your own work, its strengths and weaknesses, is not easy to acquire. **Evaluation** is taking place from day one — a constant dialogue is in process, often mentally, about how things are going. At the end of a project you will have to make a formal evaluation, a written report on the success of your work and the aspects which still require attention. For professional designers the real evaluation is in the marketplace — if you and I like their work we shall buy it. If it does its job well, we may purchase an identical replacement when it wears out. As a result the manufacturers will sell more, increase profits and may well employ the designers again.

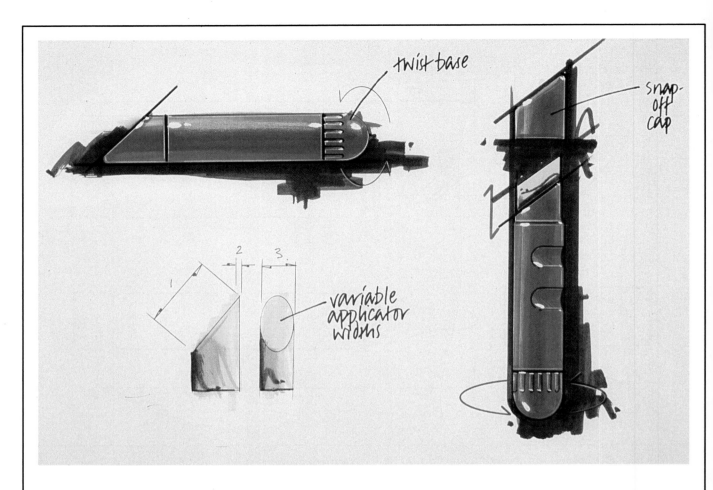

twist base

snap-off cap

variable applicator widths

Once Graham had completed his design work on the dispenser, another consultancy was commissioned to do the point of sale display design. In-house promotion and marketing teams were busy working out a product launch, press release, advertising etc. They had to make sure that the retailers understood the product and that the potential consumers were aware that there was a new and well designed alternative, with advantages over the glue which they had previously used. There was still much to do before the new product's success could be determined.

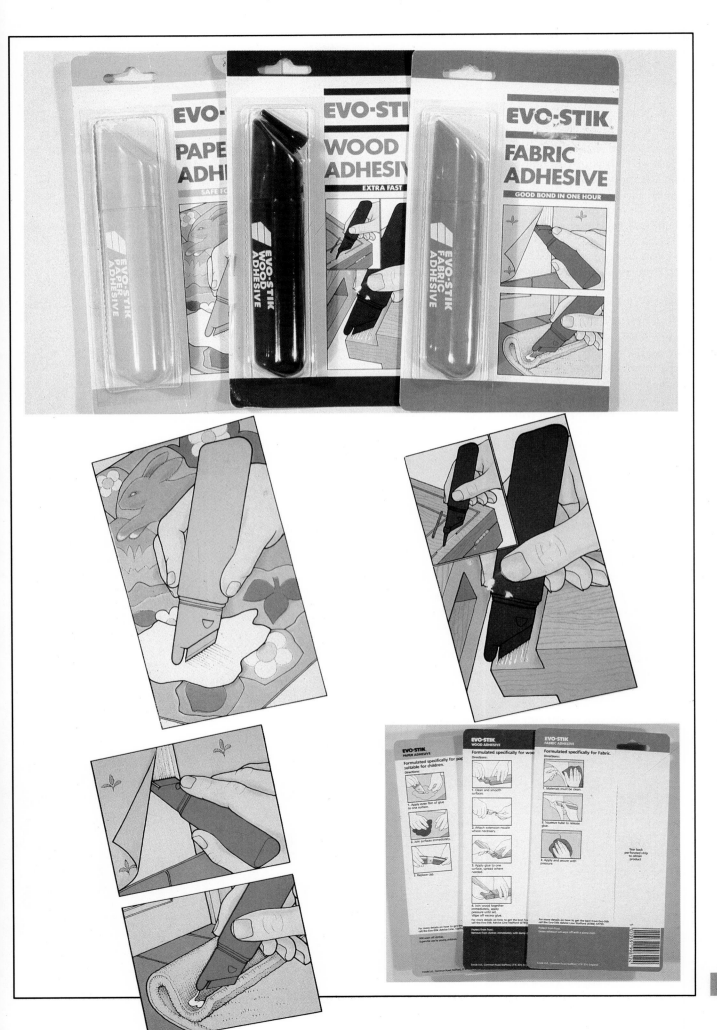

ANALYTICAL DRAWING

Sketching

A drawing is one of the best ways of recording information. Whenever you are involved in a design project, drawings will help you record all your observations, ideas and possible solutions. **Sketching** or freehand drawing is obviously the quickest and most direct method. It is something you will have no doubt practised a great deal. It is an essential skill.

You will quickly discover what medium you prefer to draw with. It may be a pencil, biro or plastic-tip pen. There are no rules, use whatever gives you the best result. Do remember that very few pens and markers allow mistakes to be corrected – this is one of the main advantages of pencils.

Layout paper is the cheapest paper and the stock in trade of most designers. It is available in different weights. A lightweight pad is more translucent and is useful when using underlays. The lighter the paper, however, the quicker the surface will break up when using an eraser or masking paper. Layout paper also has a smooth surface. If you prefer a paper with greater **tooth** (rougher texture) try using cartridge paper. Always remember if you are using spirit based pens to rest your paper on a piece of card or something similar to prevent bleeding through.

Activity 1

Experimental sketching

Let's start by experimenting with the kinds of marks we can make. Copy the texture in the boxes opposite. These have been done with a range of media. These patches of texture have a nice quality if they are not enclosed within a box; if you find you have difficulty in estimating a square use a template. Once you have copied the textures shown here, produce some more of your own. These experiments will help you to discover just what you can do with a pen or pencil!

Activitity 2

Try drawing a grid like the one shown. The proportions and arrangements of the line can vary. Try with simple shading to make the surface look three-dimensional. The first step is to decide on the tonal value in each rectangle, then shade each rectangle accordingly. Finally, try to add the shadow. If you find it difficult try making a simple model as shown. When you have mastered an ordinary shaded view, have a go using textures created with either a pen or a pencil.

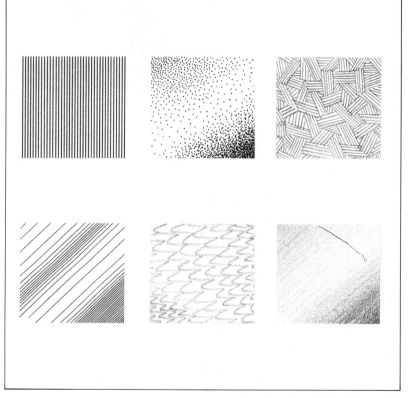

Activity 3

Sketch some cubes, then try using various textures to render the views. Remember the following:

- When sketching think only about the direction of a line, let other lines determine its length.
- The three surfaces on a cube will appear differently according to the amount of light each reflects. There will be a light, medium and dark face according to the position of the light source.

When you have done two or three cubes start making your shapes more complicated. Start introducing some curved surfaces. See if you can work out how the textures can be adjusted to fit this type of surface.

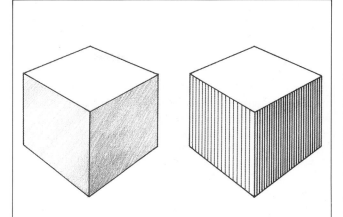

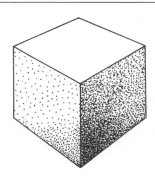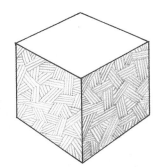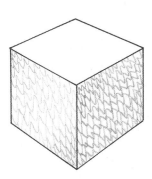

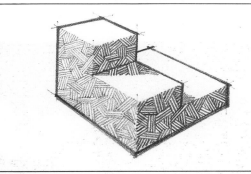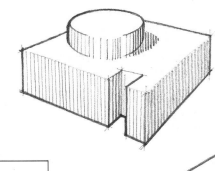

Activity 4

Use texture and line to create shapes that appear to grow out of the landscape. It is a good idea to plan your drawing first in pencil and then execute the final drawing in ink. The illusion of depth is created by exploiting the way the light falls on the object and the shadow which the object casts. Study the example and then try to do a similar drawing for a cuboid, a sphere and a cylinder.

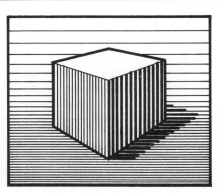

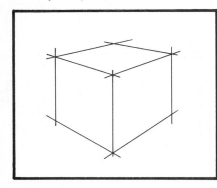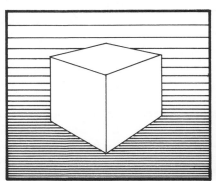

Designers' sketches

Sketching is the best way to help you explore an idea or a solution. All designers, architects, engineers or textile designers, for example, use sketches as a means of giving their ideas some substance, a starting point from which they can work towards a solution. Sketches also ensure that ideas are recorded for reference.

These sketches demonstrate early stages in the development of two design projects.

The first is a sketch by Sir Alex Issigonis of what became the Morris Mini Minor. It included a wide range of imaginative concepts and set new standards in car design. The sketch perspective shows you what the car looked like when it went into production. It is the best selling British car of all time. It is now almost thirty years old and has undergone many changes.

The second shows two early concept sketches for a chair designed by Ferdinand Porsche. The chair is called Antropovarius and ergonomic considerations were vital in its development. The designer describes it as 'an armchair with articulated structure for a perfectly anatomical, body-moulding form; through a system of adjustable "vertebrae" the chair may be adapted to a large number of body positions'. It is easy to see where the designer's inspiration came from. The final form of the chair illustrates the developments that have taken place. To achieve the designer's objective the latest carbon fibre technology had to be used. The design may be complex but the rest is easy!

THE AUSTIN MORRIS MINI 1959
Designer – Sir Alec Issigonis

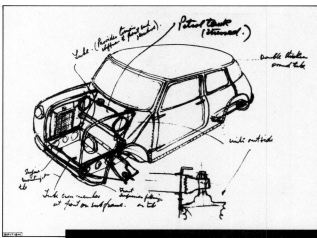

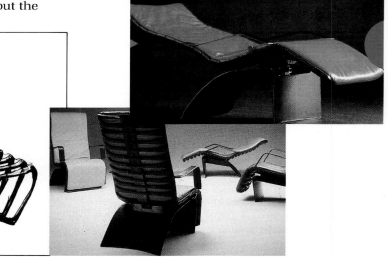

Activity 5 _____

Draw an enlarged sketch (A4 size) of the 1959 production version of the Mini. Look carefully at a current model of the car and record with annotated sketches the changes that have taken place. Produce, using either tracing paper or acetate, an overlay to attach to your sketch which illustrates these changes.

Activity 6 _____

Ask your science teacher if the school has either a part or whole skeleton which has an example of an articulating (flexible) joint. Sketch the joint carefully noting how the elements are held together and how the movement is achieved. Now look for a manufactured example of a flexible joint. You will find many examples in the school workshops and science laboratories. Make some similar analytical sketches. Note the comparisons between the two joints.

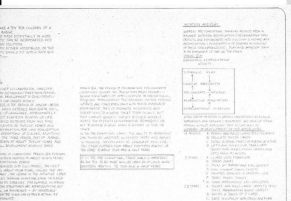

Designing from nature

Activity 6 involved looking carefully at a natural object and recording carefully what you saw. Many of our solutions to design situations owe a great deal to the natural world — it is a rich resource. It may help us to solve functional problems as in the example of the Antropovarius chair or provide inspiration when searching for visual solutions. These design sheets illustrate how accurate observation pays off. The initial drawings of the duck contain a great deal of detail. Drawings like this help the designer to develop an intimate knowledge of the subject, so that when it is simplified into a stylized form it still contains a convincing degree of realisim. Follow these design sheets through — they show clearly how to tackle a project of this type.

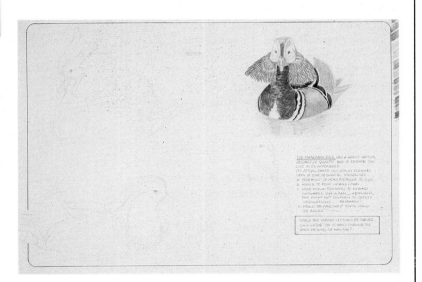

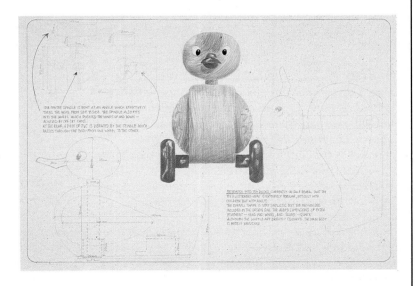

Activity 7*

Design a toy based on a study of something in the natural world. The toy can be three dimensional such as the pull-along one shown here or two dimensional such as a stylized jigsaw puzzle. Before you start, prepare a detailed specification, making sure it includes information about the potential users. Present your finished solution in the form of a presenation drawing. For this activity it is not necessary to produce a working drawing.

Product analysis — analytical sketching

Sketching is often a process by which we record the bare essentials of an object or view. It is therefore important to be economic with the lines you use to define an object as this will save you time. Here are some guidelines which are worth remembering:

- Select the view you are going to draw carefully. It should show the main features of the object in the most informative way.
- You may have to draw more than one view so think carefully before you start and decide how best the views can be drawn in relation to each other.
- Start by getting the proportions of the object correct — sketch the box or crate into which it will fit.
- Study the object carefully, trying to forget what it is and what it does. Try to view it as a series of lines and planes — record these as accurately as you can.
- Add shade and texture only if it helps reveal the true shape of the object.

Follow through the examples of the two chairs shown below. The first is composed of planes and verticals. It does not require any shading — its form is obvious from the line sketch. The second, a chaise longue, is quite curvaceous and the shading has helped to make the form more distinct.

Activity 8

Select three different chairs that you use either at school or at home, and produce an analytical sketch like the one shown here. Annotate your drawing with comments about the success of the design.

- *What is the function of the chair, what particular activity was it designed for?*
- *Does it satisfy that need, is it comfortable, does it allow the task/activity to be carried out successfully?*
- *What is it made of, how well is it made, will it prove to be safe and durable?*

There are many other questions you can ask when analysing a product. Remember to be positive, note the good features as well as those which could be improved. Try to comment on how the product might be improved to overcome its deficiences.

Activity 9

The three chairs illustrated on this page are all famous chairs. The first was designed by Gerrit Rietveld. It was known as the Red-Blue Chair and it was designed in 1919. The second was designed by Marcel Breuer. It is called the Isokon Long Chair after the company that manufactured it. The third chair went into production in 1962. Its designer, Robin Day, worked for Hille. It is often known as the Polypropylene Chair because that is the type of polymer from which the seat is moulded.

Below are sketches of ten more famous twentieth century chairs. See if you can discover which of the following designers was responsible for which chair. **Ettore Sottsass, Rennie Mackintosh, Charles Eames, Antoni Gaudi, Alvar Aalto, Vico Magistretti, Marcel Breur, Mies Van de Rohe, Le Corbusier, Josef Hoffman**

The thirteen designers mentioned on this page are amongst the most famous of this century. Select one of them and see what you can find out about him — prepare your own fact sheet about the person you select, including drawings of other things he has designed.

Activity 10 — Product analysis

A positive way of practising your sketching is to attempt a product analysis. The example on this page is of two hairdryers, but they are very different. The first was produced in the 1930s. The second is currently on sale in the high street. Despite being basically similar you will see from the analytical drawings that there are many differences. They are made of different materials, by different manufacturing methods, and there are differences in the ease with which they can be used. They have been drawn with an ordinary pencil and then shaded.

Select a product similar to a hairdryer, that is one which is held in the hand, and produce an analysis of the product on a single sheet of A3 paper.

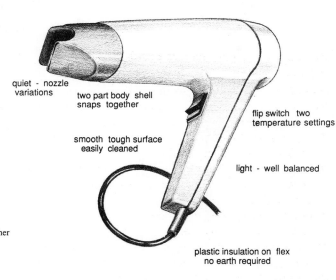

material - ABS
various bright colours

injection moulding

quiet - nozzle variations

two part body shell snaps together

smooth tough surface easily cleaned

flip switch two temperature settings

light - well balanced

plastic insulation on flex
no earth required

1980's

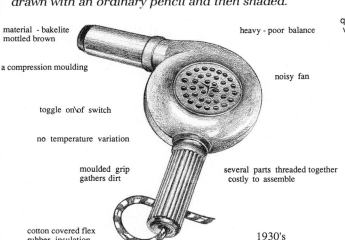

material - bakelite mottled brown

heavy - poor balance

a compression moulding

noisy fan

toggle on\of switch

no temperature variation

moulded grip gathers dirt

several parts threaded together costly to assemble

cotton covered flex rubber insulation

1930's

Product analysis – some examples

We are all consumers of design, even if we do not become professional designers. When we buy something we make conscious decisions about what we finally choose. Will it do the task it is intended for, does it look good, and can it be afforded? These are probably the three most essential questions. Each question can be expanded into a more comprehensive analysis. For example, will it do the job? By this we are asking will it perform satisfactorily, is it safe, reliable, durable, is it made of the most appropriate materials, is the construction sound, is it economic to use? The questions you ask will depend on the product. Another word for performance is **function**. When talking about a product's appearance we talk about its **form**.

Appearance or form is more subjective than function. I may like the look of something, you may not. However, there are certain criteria which can be applied, such as the proportions of the product in total, and of the various elements. Remember proportions should always be in harmony with the eventual users – people. The handle on something must not only look good, it should also be comfortable and in balance with the rest of the object. Quite often, if something looks right, it performs pretty well. Other qualities of appearance are colour and texture, although both may also be functional. An orange cable on an electric lawnmower is visually fine, and it will also show up more distinctly on grass than any other colour. Texture can enliven a dull surface. It may be decorative and it might also be an aid to grip.

Any product analysis will involve looking at the **ergonomic** aspects of a product. Ergonomics is the science of the interface between people and products. How easy is something to use, are the controls in the right place, is it comfortable to use, can it be used safely, is the weight satisfactory and balanced? These are ergonomic questions but they are similar to questions which relate to function.

Environment is another word which has many meanings when applied to product analysis. Does the product fit into the enviroment? This may mean, will the new chair fit in with the colour scheme of the curtains, carpets etc.? Or it may mean, is the new building in sympathy with those already in the neighbourhood or will it destroy the atmosphere and views? Or it could be used in the context of environmental pollution. By this we generally mean, for example, car exhaust fumes, packaging which becomes litter, or effluent in rivers. It can also refer to visual pollution. The building which becomes an eyesore is a good example!

Economic questions are also quite complex. Can I afford it, is the simple question. The initial purchase is only one aspect. Maintenance, running and replacement costs must also be considered. It might be more sensible to buy a cheap product which costs little to replace if lost or faulty rather than an expensive one. A good example is a biro. You can buy 20 to 30 of the very cheapest for the cost of one medium priced one. There is also a much wider issue: can the earth afford it? The majority of things we use are produced from finite products. The earth is the source of all our raw materials and the supply will not last forever. Conservation of resources is something we should all be concerned about. When this affects us directly we may do something about it, such as insulating our homes to lower heating bills, but we often throw away perfectly good products because they have gone out of fashion or because a better version has just been produced. We should always question where something has come from and where it is going to.

Product analysis is quite complex. A number of organizations offer help. The Consumers' Association produce *Which*, a magazine that evaluates everything which comes into our lives. Products, materials, holidays and financial decisions are all dealt with. The Design Council promotes British products which are well designed. They publish a magazine giving details of their selections and the products used to have a small black and white tag attached. Other organizations carry out safety tests and allow companies to attach approval tags if their products meet the regulations. The British Standard kitemark is the most common.

Types of analysis

There are three main ways in which products can be analysed:
1 A detailed analysis of a single product which looks closely at every aspect of it.
2 A comparative analysis of a number of products which all attempt to do the same thing.
3 An historical analysis of a present-day product compared with an out-of-date version.

All three are worth doing but for different reasons. The first may be informative in telling you how a designer tried to meet a brief. The second might help you decide on the best buy for you. The third would illustrate changes in technology and style and might help you make predictions about the future. The hairdryers on page 19 are an example of this.

Activity 11 _____

There is a range of product analysis sheets on this page: peelers, can openers, lighters and safety knives. Select a similar product, one which you can borrow four of, and carry out a comparative analysis. From your tests produce a recommended best buy.

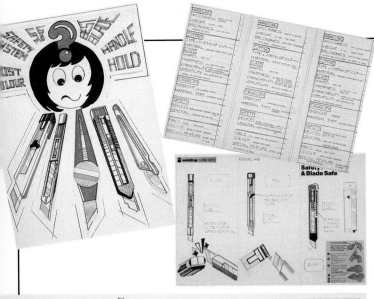

PRODUCT ANALYSIS

...OR OPENERS ....

...AN & BOTTLE OPENER — 90p

...these handles provide a comfortable... and this reasonably priced can opener is... easy to use. However, the cutting action... efficient. To halfway round the can lid... opened portion of the lid begins to... the cutting wheel loses its grip and it... impossible to complete the cut... edge is smooth, but this is hardly an... (when inevitably, you have to prise... open on an incomplete cut... useless. Be prepared for time wasting...

...WALL CAN OPENER — £5.49

...that this can opener is fixed to the... that once the can is in position, you... one hand to operate it (handy when... soup at the same time!) The can too... position until you are ready to release... gives a smooth clean cut and is easy... opener slides onto a bracket fixed... ...and ideally should be simple enough... for cleaning purposes. A tight 'fit'... that this is not always the case and the... advantage of this opener is the... in keeping it stable... convenience of a wall fixed can opener... availability—no need to go searching...

...convenient and easy to use but... accumulation of stale food.

QUICK LIFT CAN OPENER — £1.90

This is a cheaper (Hong Kong) version of the W.K. "Lift Off" can opener. The unique cutting action cuts through the side wall of the can and grips the lid until you free it to drop it in the bin. It is reasonably easy and comfortable to use, and gives a clean edged cut. It does, however, leave a sharp edge which is potentially dangerous.
The main disadvantage is that by removing the rim with lid, the tin becomes 'floppy' and awkward to handle particularly where the contents are liquid in nature.
VERDICT — Efficient, but handle with care.

TRADITIONAL CAN/BOTTLE OPENER — APPROX 80p

The plastic handle gives a comfortable grip, and with no mechanical operation to wear out or breakdown (other than the user!) this model will last for many years. The piercing blade is inclined to become blunt after some years of use when some force is required to pierce the tin.
The main disadvantage is that unlike the other openers reviewed, the can needs to be held, and as the cut edge is jagged and sharp it can be dangerous.
VERDICT — Efficient but dangerous. Better perhaps as a standby.

CONCLUSION: Apart from the Quick Lift can opener all models required one to fish the lid out of the tin or, if left hinged, to prise it open. As none of them seem to have overcome the danger of sharp or jagged edges, the Quick Lift can opener is perhaps the safest to use because the lid can be removed and put in the bin without ever being handled.

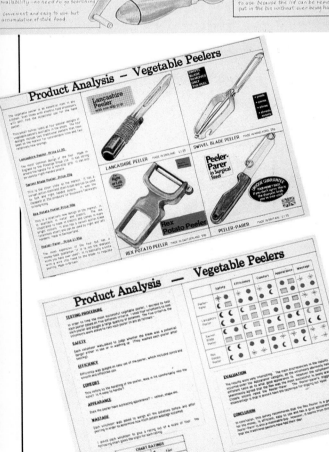

PRODUCT ANALYSIS OF POCKET LIGHTERS

RATINGS KEY: GOOD — QUITE GOOD — O.K. — POOR — BAD

Key To Features
1. DETACHABLE TOP
2. FLINT REPLACEABLE
3. REFILLABLE
4. ADJUSTABLE FLAME
5. FUEL CUT-OUT SYSTEM
6. GUARANTEED
7. SAFE REFILLING
8. SHOCK PROOF
9. DETACHABLE BASE

	A	B	C	D
PRICE	£4.50	£1.50	£2.00	£10.00
FUEL	PETROL	GAS	GAS	GAS
MATERIALS	STEEL / BRASS	STEEL / BRASS	STEEL / PLASTIC	STEEL / PLASTIC
Method of Ignition	WICK / FLINT	FLINT	FLINT	PIEZO ELECTRIC
SIZE	8 x 25 x 65 mm	25 x 15 x 80 mm	25 x 15 x 75 mm	26 x 8 x 75 mm
FEATURES	1,2,3 + 9	4,5,7 + 8	3,5,7 + 8	3,5,6,7 + 8
SAFETY	POOR		QUITE GOOD	
DURABILITY	GOOD	GOOD	GOOD	
RELIABILITY		GOOD	GOOD	POOR
EASE of USE		GOOD	GOOD	GOOD

SAFETY (A) Re-filling is quite dangerous, very easy to over-fill which causes a flare-up of fuel when lit. This can be avoided by using excess fuel time to evaporate. (B) On high flame setting the flame is 4 inches high. This is not only unnecessary but dangerous. (C) Quite good, but finger is close to flame whilst lighter is alight. Can it is... with the disposables. (D) Lighter prone to flare-up especially when fuel is low.

DURABILITY (A) "Posh" lighter. This lighter is serviceable which makes possible repairs when things go wrong. (B) Disposable. This lighter is able to run out of gas before mechanical problems set in. (C) Clipper. Similar to disposable but can be re-fitted, although cannot change the flint. Robust and shock proof. Flint is likely to go first. (D) Piezo Electric. Air would expect better. Piezo electric mechanism. Compression of quartz crystal creates a voltage to produce a spark cannot be replaced. Once crystal is compressed no point where it no longer gives off voltage strong enough for spark. Lantern life is finished. Vulnerable areas are protected, although switch is vulnerable.

RELIABILITY (A) When well fueled and set right, lighter works well; nearly every time. The disadvantage is as wick dries out lighter becomes a little less reliable. Small shock to lighter (i.e. knocked off table) might move flint, causing a jam around wheel. (B) Lights nearly every time. First time as does (C). (C) Rarely lights first time, but gets there in the end. Eventually. This is common with these lighters. Again, a poor show considering the cost.

SUMMARY Best Buy: The best value for money is the "Clipper Re-fill Lighter" (C). There is a good use of modern thermo-setting plastics which are resistant to flames and is robust. Design is uncluttered and there is a good choice of colours. Re-filling is clean and simple by injecting liquid-gas into base. WORTH CONSIDERING: French lighter. A very attractive lighter; slimline, durable and serviceable but its "poor" safety is a serious drawback. WORST BUY: Piezo Electric. High cost compared to other lighters tested, poor safety and failure to light first time is a nuisance.

ORTHOGRAPHIC DRAWING

Orthographic projection

This method of drawing is one with which you are probably already familiar. An **orthographic projection** consists of two or more two-dimensional views of an object arranged in accordance with a set of rules.

There are two types of orthographic projection: **first angle** and **third angle**.

Below are three views of a torch: a **front elevation**, an **end elevation** and a **plan**. As they appear at present they are three unrelated views. As they have not been drawn in orthographic projection, it is difficult to work out the relationship of the three views and to build up a mental picture of what the complete torch will look like. Let us look at how the torch will appear in each of the two projections.

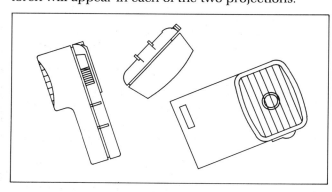

First angle

In first-angle projection the following rules apply:
- The elevations appear above the XY line.
- The plan view is below the XY line.
- The left-hand end of the object is seen in the end elevation to the right of the front elevation.
- The right-hand end of the object is seen in the end elevation to the left of the front elevation.
- The front elevation is the most important elevation and is always positioned directly above the plan.

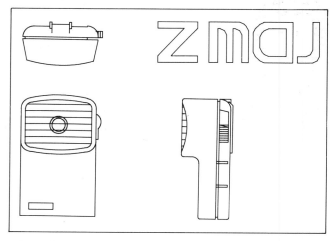

Third angle

In third-angle projection the following rules apply:
- The elevations lie in a horizontal line and are below the XY line.
- The plan view is above the XY line.
- The left-hand end of the object is seen in the end elevation to the left of the front elevation.
- The right-hand end of the object is seen in the end elevation to the right of the front elevation.
- The front elevation is the most important elevation and is always positioned directly below the plan.

In each case, if you understand orthographic projection, it is now possible to build up a picture of what the object looks like. The key fact is being able to read and understand the language of orthographic projection — try to get as much practice as you can.

Activity 12

Here are three more views of a different torch; redraw them in both first and third angle.

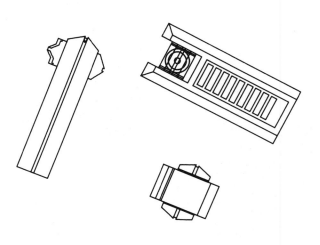

Activity 13

These views have been drawn on a BBC Master series microcomputer. No additional software has been used — the views have been drawn using the basic graphic commands. At first it takes a long time, but very quickly you can become expert. If you have access to a computer, have a go at drawing a simple object in orthographic projection using either this method or a simple Logo program.

This short program will get you started. It is the orthographic views of a simple block into which you can add detail.

```
 10 MODE 0
 20 REM front elevation
 30 VDU 29, 800;700;
 40 MOVE-300,200:DRAW300,200:DRAW300,-200:
       DRAW-300,-200:DRAW-300,200
220 REM end elevation
230 VDU 29, 200;700;
240 MOVE-100,200:DRAW100,200:DRAW100,-200:
       DRAW-100,-200:DRAW-100,200
420 REM plan
430 VDU 29, 800;200;
440 MOVE-300,100:DRAW300,100:DRAW300,-100:
       DRAW-300,-100:DRAW-300,100
```

Line 10 sets the mode — mode 0 will produce a drawing with the highest resolution. REM is short for reminder. The computer takes no notice of this line, it is there to remind the programmer what the next section of the program refers to. The VDU 29 command repositions the graphics origin. Normally 0,0 is in the bottom left-hand corner, but this command allows you to position it anywhere on the screen. It is placed, in turn, in the centre of each of the three views. Line 40 moves the graphics cursor to a corner of the elevation and then draws the four sides of the box in turn. A 180-line gap has been left. This will give you space to add detail to your front elevation. The program then goes through the same sequence to draw the crate for the end elevation and plan.

The next program will draw a simplified front elevation of a camera. It will not fit in the above front elevation crate, but the program can be adapted if you wish to work from this view and add end elevations and plans. Only by typing in this program will you discover what the camera looks like!

```
 10 MODE 0
 20 REM front elevation
 30 VDU 29, 800;700;
 40 MOVE-300,200;DRAW300,200:DRAW300,-200:
       DRAW-300,-200:DRAW-300,200
 50 MOVE0,0: PLOT 149,100,100
 60 MOVE0,0: PLOT 149,90,90
 70 MOVE0,0: PLOT 149,70,70
 80 MOVE-300,200:DRAW-450,-200:
       DRAW-450,-200:DRAW-300,-200
 90 MOVE165,0:DRAW60,250:DRAW-60,250:
       DRAW-165,0
100 DRAW-120,-160:DRAW120,-160:DRAW165,0
110 MOVE-180,200:DRAW-180,240:DRAW-220,240:
       DRAW-220,200
120 MOVE-180,40:PLOT 149,-180,60
130 MOVE 270,200:DRAW270,235:DRAW200,235:
       DRAW200,200
140 MOVE-160,40:DRAW-160,120:DRAW-180,120:
       DRAW-180,60
150 MOVE 200,-120:PLOT 149,215,-120
160 MOVE 95,160:DRAW-95,160:MOVE300,-180:
       DRAW-300,-180
170 MOVE 300,200:DRAW340,200:DRAW340,170:
       DRAW300,150
180 MOVE 320,185:PLOT 149,320,195
190 MOVE-450,200:DRAW-490,200:DRAW-490,170:
       DRAW-450,150
200 MOVE-470,185:PLOT 149,-470,195
210 MOVE-430,200:DRAW-430,240:DRAW-320,240:
       DRAW-320,200
220 MOVE-185,240:DRAW-185,260:DRAW-215,260:
       DRAW-215,240
230 MOVE 300,130:DRAW110,130:MOVE-300,130:
       DRAW-112,130
```

The only new command in this program is PLOT 149. This is the command for drawing circles. It must be preceded by a MOVE command which establishes the centre of the circle, and followed by the coordinates of a point on the circumference to set the radius.

If you do not have the facilities to do this activity using a computer, work from one of the illustrations provided and produce an orthographic projection of one of these possible designs for a futuristic instant camera.

Orthographic views

It is not always necessary to draw complete orthographic projections. An **orthographic view** is simply a two-dimensional view of an object. It is much easier to draw than a three-dimensional view and can be rendered using straightforward techniques to produce realistic visuals of a product or a building. It is a good method for investigating the shape of something being designed or the arrangement of detail within a basic outline. Normally it is the front elevation which is selected for this type of view. The front elevation shows the length and height of the object.

Activity 14*

The manufacturers of domestic appliances such as fridges, dishwashers and washing machines refer to this market sector as 'white goods', for obvious reasons. In 1987 Italian manufacturers started to break away from this traditional all-white look. Zanussi introduced a collection of fridges named the Wizard in metallic and marbled finishes. Indesit launched a washing machine called the Missi, so named as it was styled by Missoni, an Italian designer. It uses colour to emphasize shape and function and to brighten up a traditionally monochrome product.

Produce an analytical sketch of a washing machine. It should list clearly all the functions of the control panel such as the program selector and detergent drawer. From your sketch, make a scaled orthographic view of the front of the machine. By now you will appreciate what is required of a washing machine. The next step is to redesign this front elevation. This may mean redesigning the control panel, the detailed shape of the knobs, the surface graphics etc. Once you have an orthographic view of the elevation think carefully about how the various elements might be coloured.

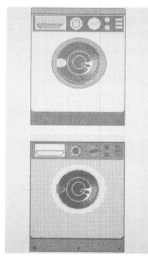

Produce a range of possibilities, either on photocopies of the outline or using a CAD system such as SuperArt. Think about machines for different markets and different tastes. Comment on the potential market by the side of each visual.

Activity 15*

The orthographic view is also an important view for the architect. An architect might be given a brief which describes the client's requirements such as detached, semi-detached or terraced, number of bedrooms and bathrooms and so on, to be built within a given budget. The architect might start by producing floor plans. It is quite likely that the overall floor area will also have been specified. The plans on these pages show the ground and floor plan of a three-bedroomed house. Your task is to draw a front elevation which will conform to the dimensions and details shown in these drawings.

Before starting there are two important decisions

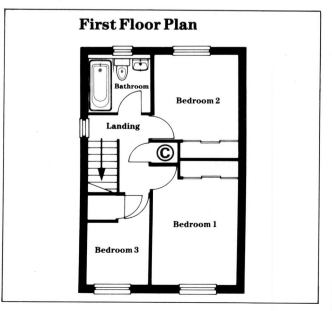

First Floor Plan

Bathroom

Bedroom 2

Landing

Bedroom 1

Bedroom 3

Ground Floor Plan

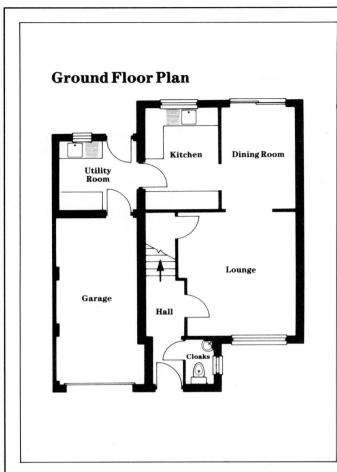

Kitchen

Dining Room

Utility Room

Lounge

Garage

Hall

Cloaks

which you must take. The first is what type of house is it to be, detached or semi-detached? It is unlikely to be terraced as it has a garage. If you wish to produce an elevation for a terraced house, modify these plans by removing the garage and utility room and repositioning the kitchen door. The other important decision is the context — in what kind of environment will the house be built? Select a building plot in your locality and make a rough plan of the area. Note the materials of which the surrounding buildings are made, what colour bricks, roofing, etc have been used? Your design must be visually sympathetic to the neighbouring buildings and landscape.

The next step is to produce the outline of the building. The dimensions do not make allowance for the space between the ceiling of the ground floor and the floor of the first floor. The height is not given for the door or the windows and the shape and type of roof has still to be determined. All these decisions and others are left to you to make.

Once you have completed the outline you must concentrate on the detail. Some more work with your sketch book is called for. Sketch details of doors and window frames found in the area, check out what is on sale in your local DIY stores, and what range of window frames might be used. When you have all this information select the most suitable and complete the elevation of your building. Use coloured pencils to complete the rendering.

Historical drawings

Designers and engineers have used orthographic drawings since about 1800 as the standard means of communicating details about a design. Frequently they used colour to distinguish between different parts of a design. You can see from the examples here how this enhanced the quality of the drawings. With the need to reproduce drawings in quantity, coloured drawings disappeared as the technology was not available to copy them. Blue-prints which showed the drawing as a white line on a blue background were the most common. With the advent of computer graphics it will be possible once again to have working drawings in colour. It is far easier to understand this type of drawing instead of one where different parts have been crosshatched.

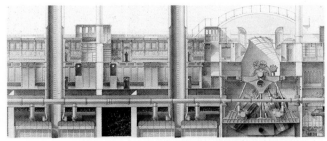

Above – a section of Brunel's design for the SS Great Eastern
Left – A blue-print of a 1924 Limousine
Below – A page from *Machine Drawing*, a 1904 textbook for engineering students in schools and colleges

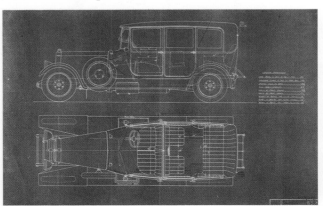

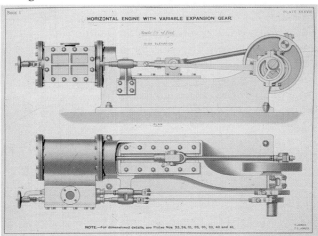

Liquid and plastic flow

To help you gain experience in orthographic projection there are a number of activities in this section. All relate to products which have been manufactured as a result of liquid or plastic flow. Before you start the activities make sure you understand how the products were produced.

Manufacturing processes — liquid and plastic flow

The vast majority of manufactured products which we use have been produced as a result of either **liquid flow** or **plastic flow**. Although not identical, these properties, and the way in which they are exploited, have many similarities. The most striking is that products made this way are made in a female mould — a cavity. The liquid or plastic material is either poured or forced into a mould, where it remains until it has set and taken up the shape of the mould, and can be removed or ejected. A simple analogy is making a jelly in a mould.

Products produced by liquid flow are generally said to have been **cast**. This is a term usually applied to metals, but cement and resins such as epoxy are also cast. Casting relies on the property of a material to flow like a liquid before setting. In the case of metal, when it is heated it melts and when it cools it solidifies. Cement and resins undergo chemical reactions, in the case of cement when water is added, and with resin when it is mixed with a **catalyst** (hardener). The addition of water or the catalyst speeds up a reaction that would occur naturally given time. Cement is also mixed with sand or aggregate before being used — this mixture is called concrete.

Casting is the starting point for a very large number of the metallic articles produced by industry. Many of the components under the bonnet of a car are produced by this method, as are the vices in your school workshop and a wide range of door furniture — handles and hooks. The mould can be made of sand (sand casting), metal (die casting) or investment plaster (lost-wax casting). Concrete can be cast directly into holes in the ground, as when pouring foundations — the earth provides the mould. When upstanding parts of a building are being cast, shuttering is used. This may be softwood, plywood or expanded polystyrene foam. Often the texture of the shuttering can be seen on the finished building. The most famous epoxy resin casting is the nose cone of Concorde. Polyester resins are used in glass reinforced polymer (GRP) products. (Polymer is the correct term for plastic.) In this process the mould, which may be either male or female, has glass matting laid on it which is then inpregnated with the resin. In commercial production the resin and glass may be pre-mixed and then sprayed onto the mould. This is far more efficient. Car panels, canoes and chairs are examples of products made this way.

A polymer does not become liquid with the addition of heat. One group, **thermoplastics**, becomes plastic with the addition of heat. This means that the material will behave like Plasticine. It is not liquid but it can be formed and shaped with pressure and forced into a mould. This process is **injection moulding** and it is rapidly becoming the single most important manufacturing process. All the castings of our domestic appliances are formed in this way — computer casings, storage systems, suitcase shells, and so on. The mould is made of metal and the process is fully automated, the moulding machines running 24 hours a day. Granules of the polymer are fed from a hopper into a heating chamber. When plastic they are forced by a screw into a mould. Compression moulding is similar but it uses **thermosetting** polymers. Once formed these cannot be reshaped. The material starts as a monomer, and is heated before being transferred to the mould. The heated mould is closed on the polymer, great pressure is exerted and the polymer is formed to the mould shape. During this process of heat and pressure **polymerization** takes place. Electrical fittings and plastic plates are good examples of this process. The 1930s hairdryer was produced by compression moulding whereas the 1980s model was injection moulded.

Activity 16

The end support of a seat for parks and playgrounds is to be cast in concrete. Wooden slats will link the two end plates. Design a concrete casting to meet this need and produce an orthographic drawing.

Pay particular attention to the size and proportions of the seat, the mountings for the wooden slats and the castings roots.

CASTING

ARCHAEOLOGISTS AND DETECTIVES USE **CASTING** TO RECORD IMPRESSIONS IN EARTH, ROCKS, ETC BY TAKING PLASTER CASTS.

WE ALSO USE SAND TO **CAST** METAL SHAPES...

AND BUILDERS POUR CONCRETE INTO PLYWOOD **MOULDS**

AIRCRAFT, CARS, BOATS. ETC ARE OFTEN MADE FROM RESINS REINFORCED WITH GLASS STRANDS (**G.R.P.**) LAID UP (LAMINATED) IN A **MOULD**.

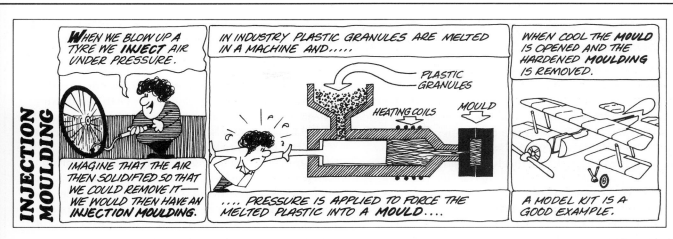

INJECTION MOULDING

WHEN WE BLOW UP A TYRE WE **INJECT** AIR UNDER PRESSURE.

IMAGINE THAT THE AIR THEN SOLIDIFIED SO THAT WE COULD REMOVE IT — WE WOULD THEN HAVE AN **INJECTION MOULDING**.

IN INDUSTRY PLASTIC GRANULES ARE MELTED IN A MACHINE AND.....

PLASTIC GRANULES

HEATING COILS

MOULD

.... PRESSURE IS APPLIED TO FORCE THE MELTED PLASTIC INTO A **MOULD**....

WHEN COOL THE **MOULD** IS OPENED AND THE HARDENED **MOULDING** IS REMOVED.

A MODEL KIT IS A GOOD EXAMPLE.

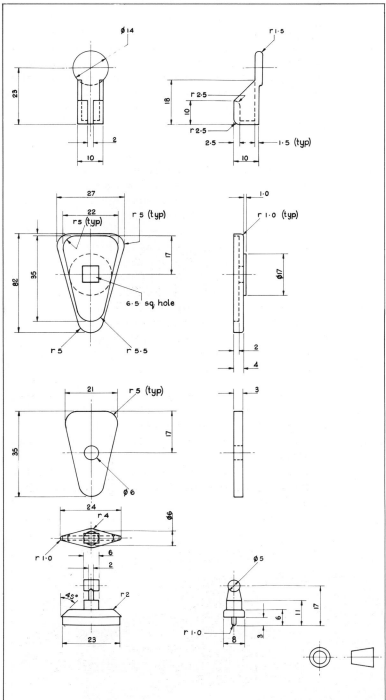

Activity 17

Select one of the following processes: sand casting, die casting, lost-wax casting, GRP manufacture, concrete casting, injection moulding and compression moulding. Find out more about the process and as a result of your investigation, produce an A4 fact sheet. Make the fact sheet as visual as possible, using monotones only so that it can be photocopied. It is a good idea if you and your friends each choose a different process. Once finished exchange sheets and you will each have a booklet — all it will need is a cover.

Activity 18*

The orthographic drawings show the details of the four components of a can sealer. The photograph shows how they fit together. When the lever, part A, is rotated through 90 degrees the two plates, parts B and C, are compressed together either side of the rip opening. Part A pivots on part D, the spindle of which passes through parts B and C.

Draw twice full-size assembled orthographic views of the device. Many food and drink packages have to be resealed after opening to maintain the freshness of the product. Carry out an investigation of the devices and gadgets which are available to do this. If you discover any that need improving or problems to which there is not yet a solution, have a go at designing an answer.

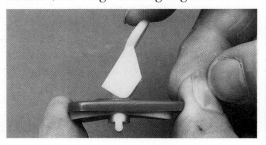

Rendering

All too frequently orthographic drawings are used just to convey accurately shape and size, which they do very well. Additionally, however, they can be used to explore design ideas. It is much easier to produce a drawing showing only the two-dimensional shape of an object rather than a three-dimensional view. Such drawings lend themselves to simple rendering techniques, using a range of media (see page 49). The rendering can be used to add form to the object, giving it a solid look. The rendering can, however, be much looser and less precise, conveying an impression of the object rather than an accurate representation.

The drawings on this page are those of Graham Thomson, the design director of Product First. Whilst working for another consultancy, Brand New Industrial Design, he designed a radio for Ross Electronics. The brief set the designer was to produce 'a product that could appear in any part of the house and not look out of place, yet not look like a conventional radio, it had to be distinctively different'.

Graham started by producing a range of options from which the company could select the most appealing for development. As you can see these ideas were in the form of orthographic drawings. The three ideas shown here are certainly very different from the typical rectangular boxes with which we are all familiar. Graham was keen to break away from what he called 'hard-edged, unsympathetic shapes'; his design evolved from a consideration of the elements that go to make up a radio. Speakers are round, as are dials and knobs, consequently these shapes became reflected in the form of the radios. Softer uncluttered forms emerged, reminiscent of the 1950s, yet totally modern and up to date.

When the manufacturer came to select a design none of these three was chosen. The one selected was a more conventional design, slightly less risky for the manufacturer. Maybe in the future Ross will bring out one of these more daring designs.

Techniques

These renderings have been produced using felt markers for the primary infill of the shape, coloured pencils for the controls, and gouache for the highlights (white fine-liner could be used instead). The first step is to produce an accurate outline. Use a fine-line biro pen that will not bleed when a marker is drawn across the line.

Next lay down the basic colour using a broad-nib spirit-based marker and roughly fill in the shape. A second marker is then used to add life and form to the drawing. In the case of the blue solution, a grey has been used whilst in the other two solutions a black has been used over a grey. The second marker was also used to add shadows cast by the buttons and to define the ground surface. The edges of the radios were then defined using a fine line black pen.

Then detail is added. The buttons were rendered using markers and coloured pencils to bring out the form. Break lines, the edges where two mouldings come together, are shown using a black line with a white reflective edge on either side. This is most easily drawn with a white pencil. A similar technique has been used around the dials and the buttons where they are set into the surface. All the remaining detail has been added, such as the speaker grill, which must be done accurately, and the tuning dial. The effect of glass on the dial has been achieved using a streaky blue marker, alternatively use a blue pastel (powdered and applied using cotton wool) and then remove reflections using an eraser. Don't be afraid to go over the edges — this gives you the freedom to express the form. You can always trim the sketch back to the sharp outline you want before mounting. Graham is obviously a master of these techniques and you can learn a great deal by looking closely at his drawings. He continued to use

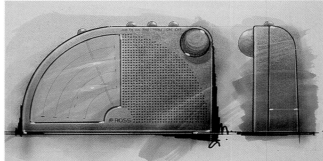

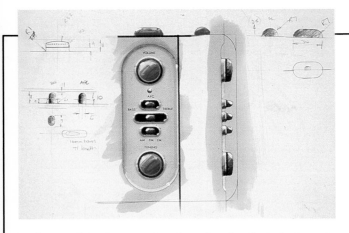

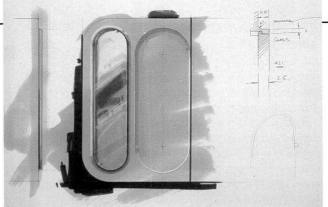

orthographic views to develop the detailed design of the selected solution. The other examples show his ideas being finalized in relation to the tuning panel and the control knobs. Accurate drawings have been rendered and dimensions established. Look carefully at these drawings and work out the rendering sequence to achieve this result.

You can see from the photograph opposite what the final radio looked like. Before this could be manufactured every moulding and item must have been drawn in orthographic projection. In one of the drawings the general arrangement or GA is shown.

Activity 19

One of Graham Thomson's ideas (top photograph, opposite page) is only shown as a front elevation. What do you think it might look like from the side? Sketch a few possibilities. For example, it might just be a prism, in which case it would have the same cross-section and its side elevation would be rectangular. Alternatively the speaker housing might be hemispherical! Select what in your opinion is the best solution, and draw it accurately, then have a go at rendering your drawing using techniques similar to those described. If you wish, draw both views and place them in correct orthographic projection.

Activity 20

Graham Thomson was also responsible for another Ross radio — the Preset. The development of the package for this radio is shown. The pack was designed by the Michael Peters consultancy. You can see how the orthographic views have been used on the pack design. Using the orthographic views of your radio, design the development of a box in which the radio will be packed.

If you have had enough of radios you can do this exercise based on any similar product such as a hot brush, staple gun or camera. Make use of a photocopier to reproduce your views and reduce them if you wish to create different effects. Your views might be rendered, using whichever technique you feel is appropriate, or you might use more technical views such as a GA or a combination.

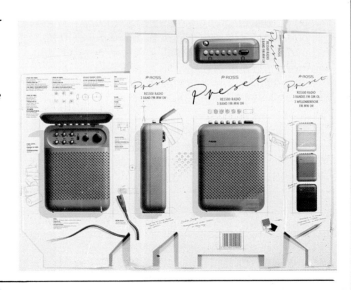

Activity 21*

What goes into a radio? Well, we know there is a speaker, a tuning panel and the control knobs, but what else? There is probably an aerial, there might be a carrying handle, both of these we can see from the outside. A radio needs an energy source. If this is derived from batteries it will need a compartment to house them. If it is to be powered from the mains it will need a transformer. Inside the casing will be the receiver. This basically consists of an input circuit for tuning into the various frequencies, the demodulation circuit which separates the audio frequency vibrations from the high-frequency carrier vibrations, and an amplifier.

These are the basic elements. The way in which the designer arranges them will be one of the factors determining their packaging — that is all the casing is. From the sizes given prepare blocks which represent each of these parts. The blocks can be made from foam, card developments or any other material which is simple and easy to work. Experiment with various arrangements recording each as a sketch. Start to consider how these elements might be wrapped. When you are satisfied that you have a good basic form, start to explore the detailing, such as the shape and position of the knobs. Work towards producing orthographic views in correct projection, either first or third, of your design for a radio. You might design your radio for a particular company. If so, look carefully at their products and see if they have a house style; if they do integrate it into your design. This will make it more realistic.

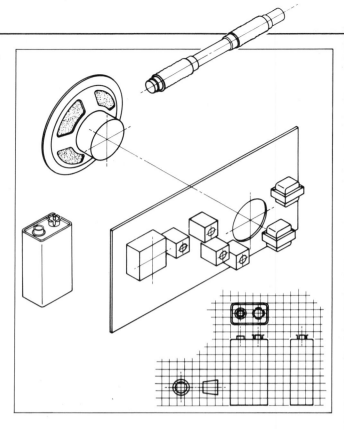

Activity 22

The photograph below and drawing (top of opposite page) are of a moulding for a dental floss container (simplified). The container has been moulded with integral hinges — marked at X and Y. Once the roll of dental floss (waxed cotton used to keep teeth and gums clean) has been placed on the spindle the container is snapped together with no additional fastenings. The accuracy of the moulding and the properties of the polymer, polypropolyene, make for a cheap yet very efficient product to both make and use.

Produce an orthographic drawing of the container snapped together. Your drawing should consist of two elevations and a plan drawn in either first or third angle projection. The end elevation may be sectioned through the axis of the spindle and the lid may be shown opened or closed.

How many other products can you identify with integral hinges? Make a study of hinges. Produce an information sheet on the various ways in which different materials can be hinged.

Activity 23

The klem clamp is a device designed to hold display panels together. It enables exhibitions to be assembled easily and quickly. Each clamp consists of two aluminium castings identical to the ones shown in orthographic projection. Two rubber inserts — one shown below — are first slipped on to the two panels. The two parts of the klem clamp are placed around them and the connecting bolt is tightened using an Allen key.

Produce assembled orthographic drawings of the clamp in correct projection. One view should be sectioned along the section line indicated. Assume a manufactured board 18 mm thick is being used. This clamp allows the boards to be positioned at an angle between 90 and 180 degrees. Can you redesign the clamp so that it will allow for positions from 30 to 180 degrees? Make an orthographic drawing of your solution.

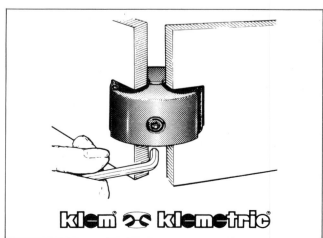

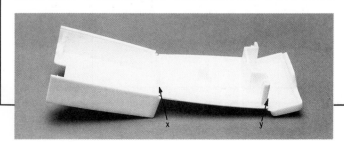

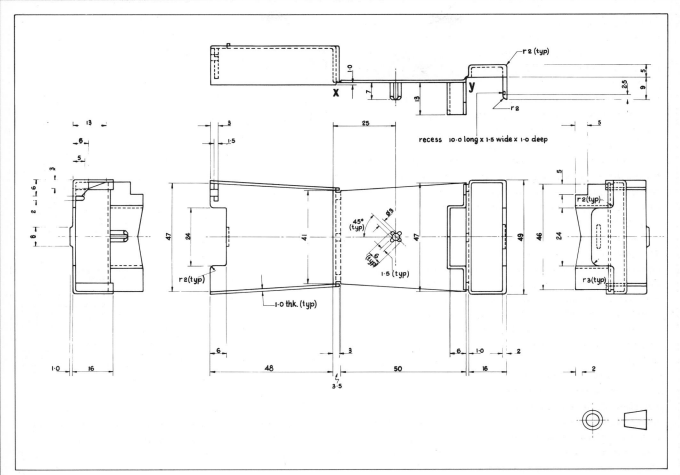

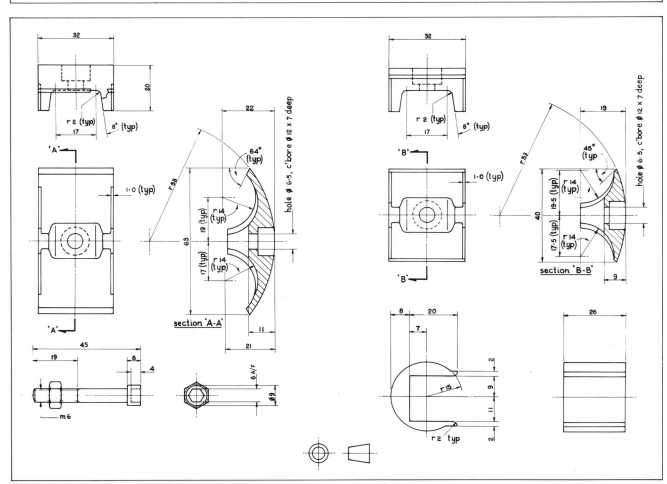

TECHNICAL GRAPHICS

Sheet material and developments

Designers frequently have to design something knowing that the finished object will have to be constructed out of **sheet material**. A car designer knows that the panels of the car must be pressed from sheet steel, a designer responsible for the form of acrylic baths knows that they will be vacuum formed. These designers rely on the property which allows certain materials to be deformed. Presses shape sheet metal by making it 'flow'; under great pressure metal sheet is forced around a male die and shaped and squeezed against a corresponding female die. Acrylic, a thermosetting plastic, becomes soft and flexible when warmed. We say it is in a plastic condition. In this state it can be shaped over a mould. A vacuum is created between the mould and the acrylic sheet. Atmospheric pressure then causes the acrylic to be pulled tightly down on to the mould.

The above processes, especially pressing metal, can be expensive. In certain situations material is bent, folded and joined to create the desired forms. This can be much cheaper if it is only a limited run or a one-off. Some materials, cardboard and fabric for example, are nearly always made into products such as containers and clothes using these techniques. The flat shape from which the final object is made is usually referred to as a **development**. However, when working with fabric, the clothing designer will call it a **pattern**.

Sheet material is usually flexible and lacks rigidity. Forming it by whatever method gives it rigidity and strength. A structure is created which is often referred to as a **shell**. Blister packs are a good example. PVC tenths of a millimetre thick is vacuum formed into transparent shells and mounted on a display board. The product can be seen, yet it is protected by the detailed shape of the blister. The contours give the thin material strength. Another example is the meat tray made from the same material. The detailed surface might also make the container attractive but principally it is there to give the pack strength.

Developments

You must be familiar with how to construct the developments for basic geometric forms. Check you understand this by running through the three examples given below: a cone, a cylinder and a hexagonal prism. With flat-sided objects, draw the true shape of each side joined to each of the other sides in such a way that it can be folded up correctly. When curved surfaces are involved, divide the surface into an equal number of parts and draw the true shape of each part.

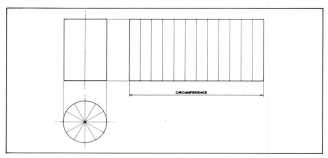

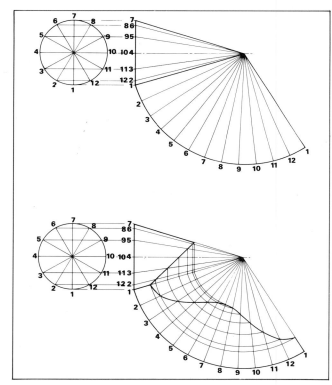

In cardboard packs or sheet metalwork the shapes required are more complex. The shape may have a hole through it or a window on one side so the contents can be seen; or the top may be cut at an angle. The first example is a pack which will contain a set of toiletries. The container is a regular hexagon. The large slant window has been designed to show all the contents. The window was drawn on the front elevation using a compass as this is the view the customer will see. Follow the stages to see how the development was calculated. First the basic shape is developed, then vectors are placed on the front elevation adjacent to the window. The vectors are numbered and transferred to the development relative to the corners of the box. The points of intersection between the window and the vectors in the front elevation are projected horizontally into the development. The points which make up the window are joined together with an accurate freehand curve; top, bottom, and joining flaps are added. The development is now ready for cutting out and testing.

The same principle can be used if the shape is cut off at an angle, in this case we say it is **truncated**. Follow the stages for the truncated cone shown below left. The cone is first developed ignoring the truncation. Its surface is divided up with a series of lines, equally spaced, from the circumference of the base to the apex. This process is known as **triangulation**. In effect we have divided the surface into a series of triangles; it is then possible to draw the true shape of each triangle and obtain the development.

The truncation is found by taking the points where the vectors cut the slope in the front elevation. Project them across to the edge of the cone (the true length of the side). Use a compass to swing the points round to the corresponding lines in the development. The points obtained can be joined up using a freehand curve. A joining flap is added and the development cut out and tested. The truncated cone is part of a hopper for feeding tube caps in a machine which screws them on to unfilled tubes.

Activity 24*

Find a cardboard pack for a confectionery product, a chocolate orange, for example. Take the pack apart and draw out the development accurately. Now rethink the graphics on the pack, including the product's name and image, and redesign the pack. Alternatively design a new product, such as a chocolate robot or lips. Model it (Plasticine covered with metal foil works well) and then design a pack for the sweet.

Before you design your sweet establish a specific market. A teenager might think that eating a chocolate hedgehog is fun but it may not appeal to everyone. The graphics will reflect the market segment identified.

Activity 25

A chain of jewellers requires a cardboard container which can be stored flat and quickly assembled to pack a customer's purchase. The container must come in three sizes and should be in keeping with the high quality of jewellery. The pack should incorporate the name of the jeweller, which you must decide.

Activity 26

Select five different objects which have been made out of sheet material. Try to include as wide a range as possible. Produce an analytical sketch of each article commenting on the material and the manufacturing process used and the reason for the finished form. Pay particular attention to the way in which strength has been achieved by shaping. Take care not to include items which have not been produced from sheet material. Many plastic shells, such as telephone casings, might look as if they have been formed from sheet but they have been injection moulded; look for the give-away sprue inlet. The other principal processes are pressing (metal), laminating (wood), vacuum forming (thermoplastics) and fabricating which is common to all materials.

Activity 27*

An estate agent has decided that a novel sales gimmick is required for an estate of new houses. He has decided to give away with each enquiry a pushout development of an example of the houses for sale. Working from a photograph of a house, a house in your locality or one you have designed yourself, produce a development of the house. The development should be easily assembled — see if you can design it so that no glue is required. It should show as much detail of the exterior as possible. Decide on an appropriate scale for your model and use colour on the final piece of artwork.

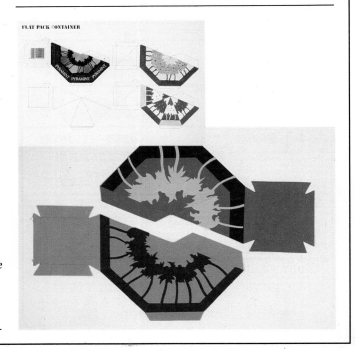

FLAT PACK CONTAINER

Machines

Without tools there would be no machines. One of the factors that distinguishes humans is our ability to fashion tools. The only **prime mover** (a machine which converts energy) available to our early ancestors was their own muscle power. So before we examine machines, let's take a look at some of the components involved.

Levers as tools

We all use tools to help us to do things better and more easily. Scissors enable us to cut paper, screwdrivers to insert screws. Although our hands are capable of doing many things they are not sharp enough to cut paper nor shaped correctly to fit a screw head. We generally take hand tools for granted, but the same implement will come in many different guises. Look at the scissors shown on this page. All are designers' solutions to the same problem, but all different. Some are more attractive to look at, others designed for particular tasks. Designers are still trying to find better solutions.

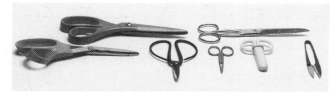

Scissors are a type of **lever**. A lever is a rod which pivots about a fixed point, called the **fulcrum**. Two forces act on a lever — these are called the **load** and the **effort**. In the case of the scissors the load is exerted by a hand, and the effort is the scissors' ability to cut. Depending on the position of the fulcrum, either a small output motion can be obtained from a large input, or conversely, a small input motion could create a large output.

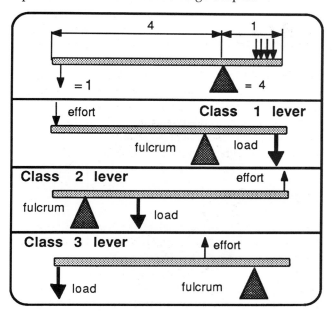

In the first case **mechanical advantage** is obtained. This means that the lever enables a large load to be moved. Tin snips used in metalwork are like this. The mechanical advantage enables you to cut sheet metal, a tough material. In the second case of small input, large output, the **movement** is said to have been **amplified**. Dressmaking scissors are like this. They have long blades and a small input will result in a long cut, ensuring lengths of fabric are cut quickly and accurately.

The effort, load and fulcrum can be arranged in three different ways, so there are three different types or classes of levers as shown in the diagrams.

Activity 28

Select one of the following groups of hand tools: hammers, saws, tongs and brushes. Find three examples of your chosen group, e.g. a toothbrush, paintbrush and handbrush. Draw each example. Now annotate each drawing describing what it is the tool is attempting to do and how this objective is achieved. Pay particular attention to ergonomic aspects. If the tool can be used in different ways, add thumbnail sketches illustrating each use. If the tool is an example of a lever, include a drawing which analyses the principle.

Activity 29

Find out more about levers and prepare an information sheet suitable for eleven- and twelve-year-olds about levers. It can take a variety of forms, e.g. a quiz, a series of experiments etc. The only two constraints are that it should be A4 and capable of being potocopied.

Wedges as tools

The **wedge** has been used by humans to solve problems since the earliest times. Axe heads, originally made of flint, are wedge shaped. On a much larger scale, an inclined plane is used to gain mechanical advantage when lifting heavy loads. A wedge is used to overcome very simple problems, for instance a piece of folded card to keep a door open. The wedge shape is also the principle behind many cutting tools. Tools cut either by cleavage or by shearing. Cleavage is where a wedge shape, usually sharp, creates such intense pressure when its edge is forced into a material that the material is forced in two just ahead of the cutting edge. Your craft knife or scalpel cuts card and plastic in this way. Scissors cut by shearing — a pair of tool edges comes together severing right through the material where the tool edges meet.

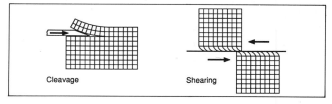

Cleavage   Shearing

The helix

If you take a right-angled, triangular piece of paper (a two-dimensional wedge or an inclined plane) and wrap it around a cylinder, with the short edge parallel to the cylinder's axis, then the hypotenuse will produce a **helix**. If you look at a cardboard tube such as the tube in the centre of a toilet roll you will see a helix. This helix has been created by the way in which a parallel strip of card has been rolled and joined to form a tube.

The helix is the basis of many devices, perhaps most importantly screw threads. An important term in relation to the helix is **pitch**. This is the vertical distance along the cylinder between each convolution of the helix. In the case of the screw thread the pitch is the distance between the crown of one screw thread and the crown of the next.

Next we need to know how to draw a helix.

1 First draw the front elevation and plan view of a cylinder.
2 Divide the plan into 12 equal parts using a 30 degree set square, number the divisions from 1 to 12.
3 Mark along the height of the front elevation three pitches of the screw thread. Divide each into 12 equal parts and number each 1 to 12.
4 Project up from the plan view, into the front elevation, the divisions on the circumference.
5 Mark the points where corresponding divisions meet. There will be three for each number if the helix has three pitches.
6 Join the points together to obtain the helix. Remember that parts of the helix go around the back of the cylinder so they will be in hidden detail.

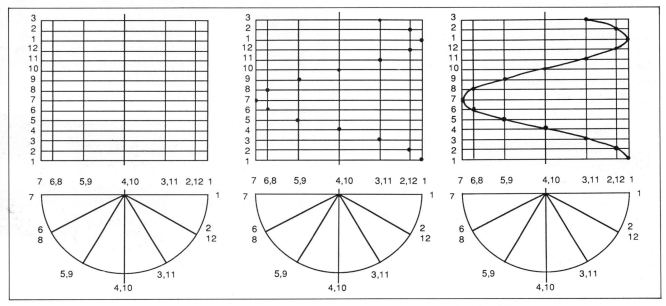

Screw threads come in two basic forms, **V thread** and **square thread**. In the V thread there are two helices, one on the root diameter of the thread and the other on the crown. In a square thread there are four, one for each corner of the square thread form. They are quite a challenge to draw. See if you can find out how to draw a screw thread.

Activity 30

1 *Construct three pitches of a helix about an 80 mm diameter cylinder, each pitch being equal to 60 mm.*
2 *A toilet roll manufacturer wishes to produce cardboard rolls 45 mm in diameter and 110 mm long The tube is to be made from card wound in such a way that the joint is a single pitch of a helix. By drawing, work out the required width of the card strip. Produce a development of a single tube. What shape is it? You may be surprised!*
3 *For the following dimensions attempt to draw a square screw thread. Its major diameter is 80 mm and its minor diameter 56 mm. Draw a minimum of two pitches.*

Screw thread applications

Screw threads have many uses. There are a wide range of fastenings which depend on screw threads, such as nuts and bolts. Cramps and vices use the mechanical advantage obtainable from a screw form to hold, press and clamp objects. A screw thread can be used to lift loads as in a car jack or a levelling device on a castor. Motion can also be transmitted via a thread, which is normally square. You will find many examples on the machine tools in the workshop, e.g. the leadscrew on a lathe or the transverse feed on a milling machine.

The helix in nature

The helix is, of course, a natural pattern which we have adapted to our own uses. Many inventions have come about from close observation of nature. The tendrils on wild clematis could well have been the inspiration for telephone cords. This is certainly the most economical way of storing a length of cable.

Uses of the helix

The photographs show a variety of examples where the helix has helped us solve a problem. In architecture the spiral staircase and the ramp in a multistorey car park are both examples where an inclined plane has been wrapped around to save space and allow access at a number of points. The corkscrew shows three different helical forms. The helical slide is a simple form of a helter-skelter where the chute is wrapped around a cone rather than a cylinder. The helical fins on the outside of the chimneys channel passing air, causing it to spiral up around the chimney, increasing in speed as it goes. The result is that the smoke or gas being expelled from the chimney is lifted on this air stream high into the atmosphere. The fabric illustrates how these forms can be used to generate decorative patterns.

The last example, a lens brush, is very interesting. If the base of the brush is rotated the brush will rise out of its protective container. The rotating motion has been converted into linear, or more correctly, **reciprocating** motion. This is achieved by a lug in the brush locating in a helical slot in the casing. As the base is turned the brush is automatically lifted, and if the base is turned in the opposite direction the brush will return to the container. The same principle is used on good quality lipsticks.

Activity 31 — Investigation

Examine the screw top on a good quality fountain pen. Count the number of threads, then the number of revolutions taken to completely tighten the top. Why is there a discrepancy in these two figures? Explain the reason. (You may find it helpful to look closely at the chimney photograph.)

Investigate the double helix. What have the names Crick and Watson to do with it?

Activity 32

Use the helix as a pattern for the decoration of a coffee mug. The decoration must be applied using only two colours other than white. The dimensions for the mug are given in mm. Produce a coloured elevation of your design.

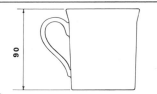

90

⌀ 75

Activity 33

A cosmetic manufacturer requires a design for a lipstick casing so that the lipstick can be controlled very precisely. The lipstick is to be approximately 60 mm long by 18 mm in diameter. It should take one and a half revolutions to move from being closed to being fully out. Produce three times full size an orthographic elevation (similar to the brush photograph) of what the lipstick might look like.

Linkages and loci

A **linkage** is a name given to any mechanism that is a combination of links connected by pins. A **link** is simply a straight bar, with a hole at either end which enables it to be joined to other links and fixed points. The joint between two links can also be called a **pivot** or a **node**. A linkage is used to transmit a motion. An input at one end will result in an output at the other end.

A bicycle brake is a linkage. When the rider inputs motion into the system by squeezing the brake lever, the motion is transferred to the brake calipers which are squeezed together, causing the brake blocks to tighten on to the rim of the wheel and the bike to slow down. In this example (top of opposite page) one of the links, the cable, is flexible. The brake lever is first order and the position of the fulcrum is such that mechanical advantage is achieved; note that the calipers operate just like a pair of scissors. Another example of a linkage is a pantograph which is used to enlarge and reduce drawings; you may well have used one or even made one.

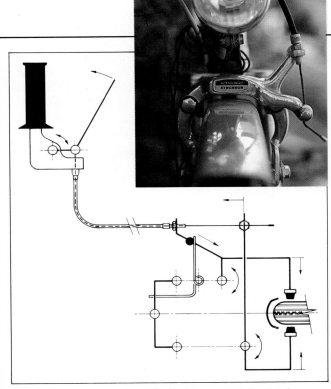

There are two principle linkages which are the basis of other more complex systems. All linkages can be broken down into two basic units. These are:

- The four-bar linkage or quadric-crank mechanism.
- The slider-crank mechanism.

Let us examine each in turn.

Four-bar linkage

This consists of four links joined by pins. The pantograph is an example. One of the bars is usually stationary. How the linkage behaves will depend on the lengths of the various arms. Some links may be capable of rotating through 360 degrees giving **rotary motion**. Alternatively the link may be constrained to rock to and fro through an arc giving **oscillating motion**. The link that rotates through 360 degrees is known as the **crank**. If two levers can rotate fully the shorter will be the crank. The stationary link is sometimes called the **frame**. The link opposite the frame in the linkage is the **coupler**.

A simple example of a four-bar linkage is the bucking bronco playground horse. The horse is the coupler, hanging on two oscillating cranks; the stationary link is the ground surface. An example where the crank rotates fully is a treadle-operated mechanism, like an old-fashioned sewing machine or the linkage which causes a fan to move to and fro. A parallel linkage, where the stationary arm and the coupler are equal in length, as are both cranks, is used on toolboxes.

Slider-crank mechanism

The nature of a crank has already been explained — it is a link that rotates fully through 360 degrees. A slider moves back and forward in a straight line, a motion which in future we shall refer to as **reciprocating**. The slider must either be connected to the rest of the linkage by a pivoting joint or it must be free to oscillate. The slider-crank mechanism converts rotary motion to reciprocating or reciprocating to rotary. A simple example is the floor mop. As the collar is pushed down the handle (reciprocating motion), the swivelling mop head is caused to rotate and is compressed against the fixed sponge, and the water is squeezed out. Another common example is the internal combustion engine. The combustion of an air/petrol mixture in the cylinder results in gases which expand and cause the piston to move down the cylinder. Acting through the connecting rod, the reciprocating motion of the piston imparts a rotary motion to the crankshaft. Four strokes of the piston are required to complete the cycle.

Loci

As a mechanism moves, points on it will trace out curves which are known as **loci**. The simplest locus is the trace produced by a single link rotating around a fixed point. As you know, this locus has a special name — a circle. Engineering designers will plot loci to ensure that a mechanism is going to move in the correct path or to check that it will not interfere with other parts of the machine. A locus can be determined in one of two ways; either by drawing the mechanism in a number of positions during its cycle, or by using a trammel. These alternatives are similar to the two ways in which you have already learnt to construct an ellipse.

Activity 34

The diagram shows a schematic view of a desk stay. The stay is fixed to the lid at A about which it is free to pivot. The stay always passes through a sleeve at point B. Plot the path traced by the end C of the stay as the lid moves from the closed to the open position. What is the angular movement of the lid?

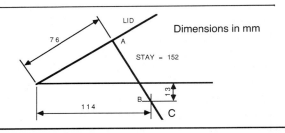

LID

Dimensions in mm

76   A

STAY = 152

114   B   13

C

Activity 35

Below is a drawing of a link mechanism. AD and CB are links pinned together at C. The pivoted joint B allows the link BC to travel along the line EF. Plot the locus of D for one revolution of AB.

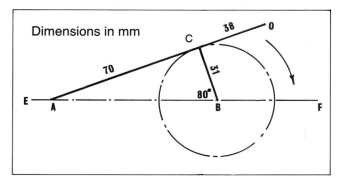

Dimensions in mm

Activity 36

Linkages can be used in simple toys such as the pecking chickens shown in the photograph. The linkage which makes it work is the same as for the toolbox, a four-bar parallel linkage. In this instance the motion is input into the system by flexing the spring handle. There are other ways in which the chickens can be made to peck, for example using a pendulum. Design a toy like the chickens. First draw out the linkage and plot what will happen when the mechanism is in motion. Model the principle in card, then if you have the time and facilities make a working model. Thin strips of wood and dowel or alternatively plastic tube could be used.

What will happen if the linkage is not composed of parallel links? Will this result in different types of movement? Try it and find out!

Activity 37

In the pecking chickens the cranks both oscillate, neither rotates. Attempt to animate a figure using a linkage in which one crank rotates. Follow the example given and then try yourself. The first step is to find a figure. Cartoon characters are a good idea. In this case a man is going to lift his nightcap and a caption is going to appear saying 'sweet dreams'. The rotary motion of the handle (crank) is going to be translated into oscillating motion by the linkage. The coupler, extended in two directions, will be the arm which will lift the hat and the appearing caption.

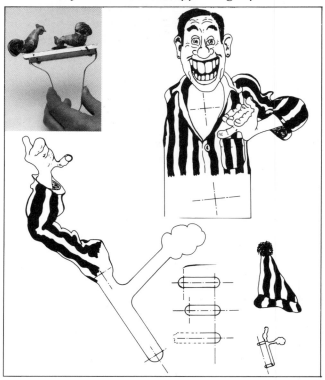

A pin and scrap card model is used to determine how the linkage will operate. These materials are easy to experiment with and a solution which works will soon be found. The individual components can then be drawn out accurately. Use photocopies of your original artwork so that it is not destroyed. Mount the paper shapes on card and cut out the final pieces. Use a leather punch to make holes where rotation or oscillation will occur; make sure a slit is used to connect the handle to the crank. Paper fasteners or velos eyelets are ideal for the pins. Assemble your figure and see if it works.

Cams, pulleys and gears

Cams

A **cam** is specially shaped so that its edge will cause another part to move in a particular way. Most commonly the cam is fixed to a rotating shaft and causes the follower to rise and fall in relation to its profile. A familiar example is the camshaft in a petrol engine. The rotating shaft has a number of cams on it, two per cylinder. Each pair opens and closes the inlet and exhaust valves for each cylinder. All the cams are identical, but they are machined at different attitudes so that the valves open and close in the correct sequence. The camshaft has converted rotary motion into reciprocating motion.

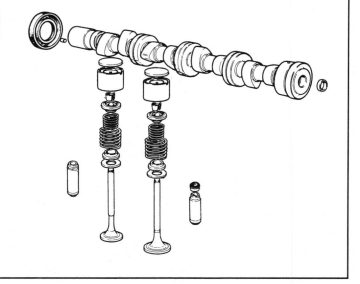

Another example of a cam is the bottle stopper used for creating an airtight seal on a wine bottle once the cork has been removed, or on a crown cap bottle. The cam in this instance oscillates, inducing reciprocating motion in the shaft, which squeezes the rubber seal causing it to expand and block the neck of the bottle. A number of terms are used to describe the motion of a cam. These are illustrated in the diagram.

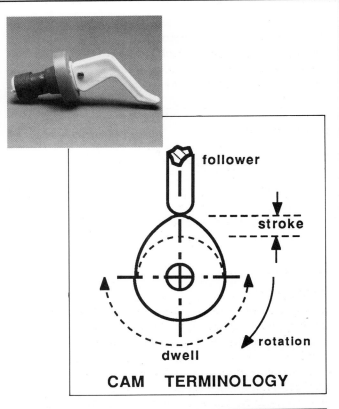

Activity 38

*The diagram shows a cross-section through a simple pull-along toy. Cams mounted on the axles cause both the driver and the passenger to bounce up and down, giving the illusion of a bumpy ride! The cam under the driver is an offset circle. This will make him rise and fall once for every rotation of the axle. This type of cam is called an **eccentric**. The passenger is having a much rougher ride and will bump up and down twice for every rotation. Your task is to design a cam which will cause the passenger to rise 10 mm on each occasion. Draw your cam four times life size.*

When designing a cam we assume the cam is stationary and that the follower is moving around its circumference. We then draw the follower in the various positions we want it to achieve. The shape of the cam can then be drawn in under the follower. When you have designed your cam make a simple model and check out the displacement of the passenger. Modify your design if it is not quite right.

If a follower is acting directly on a cam, the cam can only cause it to rise and fall the amount of the stroke. The stroke can be amplfied by using a pivoted lever. The lever will oscillate and a follower can be driven from it. The lever must be kept in contact with the cam using a spring. Can you redesign the toy to incorporate a lever which will amplify the movement of the passenger? Write other criteria for the movement of either the passenger or the driver and see if you can design a cam to achieve your brief.

Activity 39

Study the photograph of the snap-off craft knife. It is made of four injection mouldings: the main body (A), the end cap (this is also used for snapping off blunt sections of the blade), the link moulding and the blade locking lever. When the locking lever is vertical (see photograph) the blade can be slid out and a new section exposed. As the lever oscillates through 90 degrees the blade is locked in place. How do you think the locking lever works? Draw a cross-section through the knife on section line AA with the locking lever vertical, and then another with the lever in the locked position. With the aid of annotations explain clearly how the locking is achieved. Sketch two other instances where locking is achieved in a similar way. There is another example in this book in Unit 2!

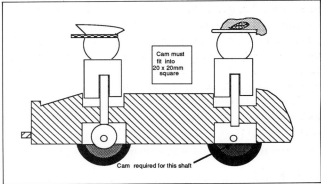

follower

stroke

rotation

dwell

CAM TERMINOLOGY

Cam must fit into 20 x 20mm square

Cam required for this shaft

Pulleys

Pulleys and **gears** are both used to transmit rotary motion. Pulleys are used when the rotary motion in one shaft is to be transmitted to another parallel shaft or axle. A pulley is a wheel with a groove in its rim in which a belt is located. Pulleys can be used to change both the relative speeds of rotation of the two shafts, and the direction of rotation. If the driving pulley is larger than the driven pulley, then the rotary velocity in the driven shaft will be greater than in the driving shaft. To slow down the relative velocities the larger pulley should be on the driving shaft. The relative sizes of pulleys is often expressed as the **velocity ratio**.

For example, if pulleys were being used simply to transmit the motion from one shaft to another with no change in relative velocity, they would be the same size and the velocity ratio would be 1:1.

If the driver pulley had a diameter twice that of the driven pulley, the velocity ratio would be 1:2. The driver pulley completes one revolution to every two of the driven pulley.

If the pulley belt is a straight loop the shafts will both rotate in the same direction. If the belt is crossed the shafts will turn in opposite directions. To avoid slip between the pulleys and the belt, a toothed belt and pulley can be used. Alternatively, a toothed wheel called a **sprocket** and a chain made of loosely jointed links can be used, such as on a bicycle.

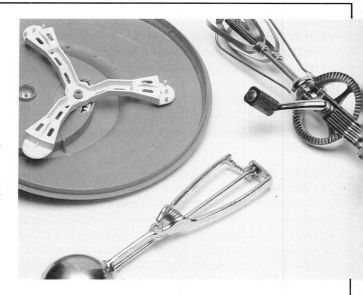

Gears

A **gear** is a wheel which has precisely machined teeth around its edge or circumference. A gear transmits rotary motion and force, and has a shaft passing through its centre. Gears are used in groups or **trains**, the gears being arranged so that their teeth mesh together. The spacing and size of the teeth on meshing gears must be the same. Simple gears are called **spur gears**. If two mesh together the larger is called the **wheel** and the smaller the **pinion**. A gear is complicated to draw so a convention is used — two concentric circles. The larger corresponds to the tip of the gear tooth and the smaller to the root of the tooth.

When describing the relationship between two meshing gears we talk about the **gear ratio**. If the driver gear has 30 teeth and the driven gear 15, it is obvious that the driven gear will rotate twice as many times as the driver. The gear ratio is said to be 1:2. If the roles are reversed and the driver gear has 15 teeth and the driven 30 teeth, the gear ratio will be 2:1.

The following examples are found in a kitchen. In the whisk the input motion turns the large gear. There are 64 teeth pressed into stainless steel. It meshes with a gear having 8 teeth mounted at right angles. The result is that the motion is turned through 90 degrees giving a vertical output motion and a gear ratio of 1:8.

The lid of the salad spinner is an example of an internal gear. The spur gear at the centre of the three-spoke moulding fits on to spindle A so that it meshes with the internal gear seen through the aperture. The spindle B is driven by the handle on the other side of the lid. The large internal gear has 77 teeth; the small spur gear has 11 teeth. One revolution of the handle will result in the spur gear rotating 7 times, a gear ratio 7:1. The result is that the lettuce is spun far quicker than could normally be achieved manually and the water is thrown off.

The ice-cream scoop illustrates how gears can be used to transform linear to rotary motion. As the handle is squeezed the rack drives the pinion which is mounted on the central spindle. This causes the semicircular blade, mounted in the scoop, to rotate through 180 degrees and release the ice-cream.

Activity 40*
Investigate where gears, cams and pulleys are to be found in the school workshop. Devise a trail (like a nature trail) which will lead someone from example to example. Produce an accompanying leaflet which will explain the mechanisms on the trail. It is a good idea to make the trail simple to start with, gradually becoming more complex.

Mechanical toys

Now you have an understanding of cams, gears and pulleys let us see how they can be used in mechanical automata. The first two design sheets show a design idea for a simple toy which operates in one plane. A fisherman is attempting to catch a fish. A spindle is turned by a handle, and two cams on the spindle drive push rods. One causes the fisherman to rock up and down and the other causes the frog to hop up and down.

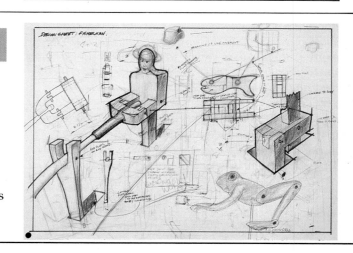

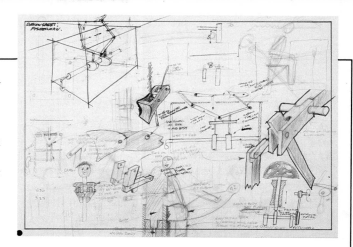

Activity 41

Make an orthographic working diagram of how this toy will work. Design suitable cams to transmit the correct motion. From your diagram make a model of the toy using card or polystyrene. Start by producing a frame in which the mechanism can be housed. It must be fairly rigid. Webs inside the box will help to shore it up. Paper rolled tightly makes good spindles and eyelets make good bearings. Dowel, tubing or rod can also be used — there are no rules, use the most appropriate material that is available.

The next three design sheets show how a mechanical helicopter was designed. Sheet 1 illustrates a range of ideas from which the helicopter was developed. The second sheet shows the idea being developed, and in particular the construction of the pilot. The final sheet illustrates the general arrangement of the system, a single input, a handle turned manually, and the result — five outputs. The seagulls circle overhead. Both rotors turn, one in the vertical plane and one in the horizontal, and the pilot moves backwards and forwards whilst his head turns. The gears are all friction gears but the model still works well. As you can see from the photograph the final product also looks pretty good.

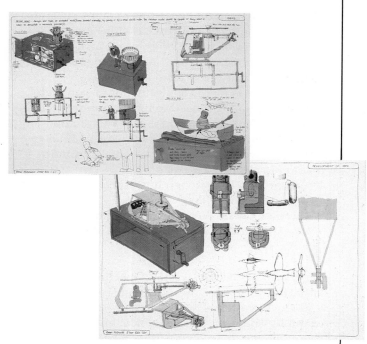

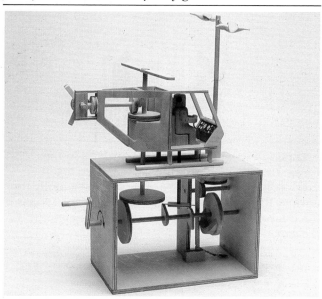

Activity 42

A company has decided to produce a number of these toys. For commercial production, friction gears might prove unreliable. To overcome this, spur gears and bevel gears will be used to ensure smooth operation. (Bevel gears have teeth cut on a cone and are used to transmit rotary motion between shafts at right angles to each other.)

Your task is to produce a working diagram to show the position of the gears and to annotate it to describe how the various outputs will be achieved. Make any modifications to the design which you think will be necessary. You may consider using overlays to illustrate how the various outputs are achieved. The size of the surrounding frame is 140 mm x 70 mm.

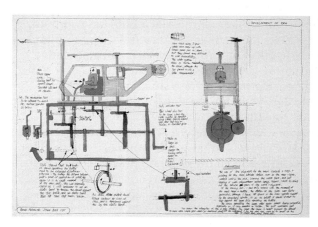

Activity 43*

Using any of the mechanical devices which you have learnt about, design and manufacture a mechanical money box or automata. You will have to work within the resources available. Discs of cards can be laminated together to make pulleys, friction gears and cams. Cocktail sticks, matches and straws are useful for spindles and eyelets make good joints and bearings. A word of advice — do not be too ambitious initially. Produce a container with a rotating shaft and then start to add to it.

Electronic control systems

In the hi-tech world in which we live electronic systems have become the prime method of control. In recent years mechanical control systems, with many moving parts, have been replaced by electronic systems based on **integrated circuits** (**ICs**). An IC, or chip as they are often called, is an electronic device containing a number of discrete components. An IC, which might contain any number of resistors or transistors for example, can be produced at a fraction of the cost of a circuit consisting of many separate components. Electronic systems allow greater flexibility and reliability, for example, look at the wide range of washing programs available to the user of a washing machine controlled in this way.

Electronics is highly complex. For design and communication you need to have an understanding of what is involved, but you do not require the same level of expertise as someone studying technology. There are two aspects which we shall look at in relation to electronics:

- Ergonomics — switches, how the circuit is physically controlled.
- Circuit diagrams — the symbols and conventions used in drawing systems.

Switches

Every product, from a washing machine to a CNC lathe, has to be controlled by the user. There is quite a variety of switches — toggle, rotary and linear for example. These are all mechanical in operation. A movement causes a connection to be made, acts as an on/off switch, or increases the flow of current, controlling the brightness of a bulb for example. These switching methods are still very common but increasingly, **membrane** or **pressure sensitive** switching is being used. Look at a CNC lathe, a drink dispensing machine or a slim credit card style calculator. All these use membrane panels to control their operation.

A membrane switch in a sense is still mechanical, as pressure has to be applied to make a connection. You can see from the diagram how it works. Two conductive surfaces are held apart by a membrane with a window in it. Pressure applied to the top causes a connection to be made, current to flow and the circuit to function. In this simple example continuous pressure has to be applied to maintain contact. If a simple circuit is produced consisting of a battery, membrane switch and either an LED (light emitting diode) or buzzer to indicate when the circuit is complete, it can form the starting point for a board game. Here are some suggestions:

- A quiz — one membrane switch adjacent to the question, and a choice of possible answers each with adjacent membrane switches. Only the correct combination will sound the buzzer or cause the LED to glow. A range of quiz mats can be made to slot on to the basic board.

- Maze type games — a series of switches which must be followed to get from one side of the board to the other.
- Spot the difference — two pictures with very minor differences. Pressure applied to the parts that differ completes the circuit.

These are just some ideas — you will probably have many others about how the simple circuit can be adapted.

Making a membrane panel game

This is very simple. The tracks are made from thin strips of aluminium foil. They are connected to the remainder of the circuit using staples. Where one track crosses another and insultation is required, use a piece of Sellotape. If you have difficulty in cutting aluminium foil accurately using spray mount, start by gluing it to a sheet of paper. You will then find it much easier to cut. Make sure when you are laying tracks that you make good contact at joints. Burnish foil strips together using your finger nail. It is a good idea to lay tracks on the base layer and then make the whole of the underside of the top layer conductive. This is wasteful on foil but saves a great deal of time.

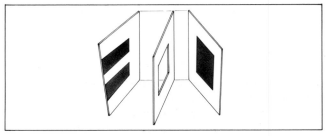

Experiment with the sizes of windows in the centre panel. The closer the switches are together, the smaller the hole will be and so consequently the thinner the layer needs to be. The larger the switch the thicker the panel will need to be to maintain the gap.

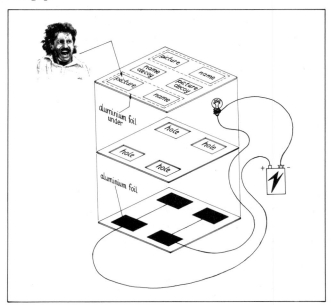

Circuit diagrams

It is essential to be able to draw electrical components quickly and easily. As in engineering drawing, a system of graphical symbols has been devised to overcome the problem of drawing complex three-dimensional forms. These symbols are two-dimensional. They can be drawn using templates, transfers or with the aid of a computer. The full range of symbols appears in British Standard (BS) 3939 and selected ones appear in PP 7302. The symbols required to carry out the activities in this book are shown in Activity 47, but there are many more. Circuit diagrams should show clearly how the various components are linked. They are always laid out in a rectilinear manner if possible. Look at the example, a pictorial view of a circuit and then two attempts at a circuit diagram. The first is poorly drawn — it is difficult to understand. The second is a correct drawing, anyone who understands the symbols could build the circuit from the diagram.

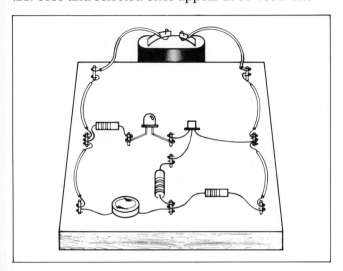

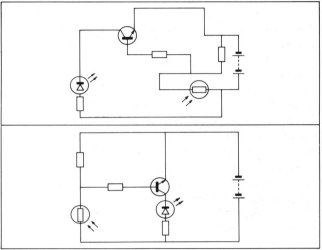

Activity 44

Design and make a game which employs membrane panel switching. The game must be no larger than A4. It should contain a minimum of eight switches. As your expertise is in graphics, pay particular attention to this aspect of the game. Produce all the associated information required to know how to play the game.

Activity 45

Conduct a survey of the different types of switching used on consumer products. Draw each one, then annotate your drawing to describe how each works. From your research select one situation where you think the switch could be replaced with a membrane panel. Redesign the appropriate portion of the product to show how the membrane panel might be incorporated.

Activity 46*

A manufacturer has decided to produce a radio with a multi-functional membrane panel control system. Do you think this is possible? Decide for yourself what aspects of a radio could be controlled in this way and design the graphics for the top layer, the part seen by the user. Pay particular attention to the placement of functions in relation to each other and the use of colour. It might be a good idea to have a look at some existing panels before embarking on this project, such as those on photocopiers or cash registers.

Activity 47

Construct circuit diagrams of the two circuits shown in pictorial form. The symbols required to do this are shown adjacent to the sketches.

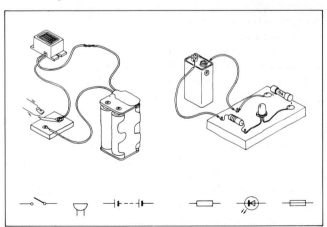

Activity 48*

Alarm systems operate in a range of ways such as pressure pads (like a membrane panel switch but placed under a carpet), infrared detecters etc. Contact a company in your area which specializes in alarm systems. From the information you receive, design an alarm system for the house in Activity 15, page 24, or alternatively your own home. Produce a circuit diagram and a list of the components etc. required to install the system.

Hydraulics and pneumatics

A mechanism is one of the simplest methods of control, making something happen remotely. The input motion is transferred through linkages, but as we saw in an earlier example, the bicycle brake, a flexible link is often required. Instead of transferring motion via links and cables it is also possible to use air and fluids. A system using air is referred to as **pneumatic**, and one using fluid **hydraulic**. You may have made simple toys using pneumatic systems (balloons and squeezy bottles) or hydraulic systems (syringes) in your foundation course. If you did, you will have appreciated the advantages, such as flexible coupling, and, in a hydraulic system, no loss of power with distance.

Only in simple switches will you find closed pneumatic systems. A remote control for a camera shutter is a good example. Open systems which are far more common in industry require a compressor and tend to be noisy. Air is used to control pistons in opening, closing and clamping devices. In some workshops compressed air is used to drive power tools.

Hydraulic systems are very efficient. The brakes on a car are hydraulically controlled. When the brake pedal is depressed the piston in the master cylinder exerts pressure on the fluid in the system. The pressure is transmitted to a series of pistons, eight in all, one on either side of each disc. There are four discs, one for each wheel. The pressure causes the pistons to squeeze the discs and slow down the car. As pressure is transmitted evenly throughout, a liquid pressure applied at one point will be divided equally between all the slave cylinders.

If the pistons at the disc have twice the area of the master piston they will exert twice the force that the driver applies with his foot. The force is magnified by the increased area of the pistons. In a hydraulic system, if the slave cylinder has a smaller cross-section than the master cylinder, then the piston will travel further than the input motion when the system is pressurized. Hydraulic systems are used in presses, jacks and lifts, for example.

The design sheets illustrate how a system using syringes can be used to model a simple robotic arm made out of corriflute.

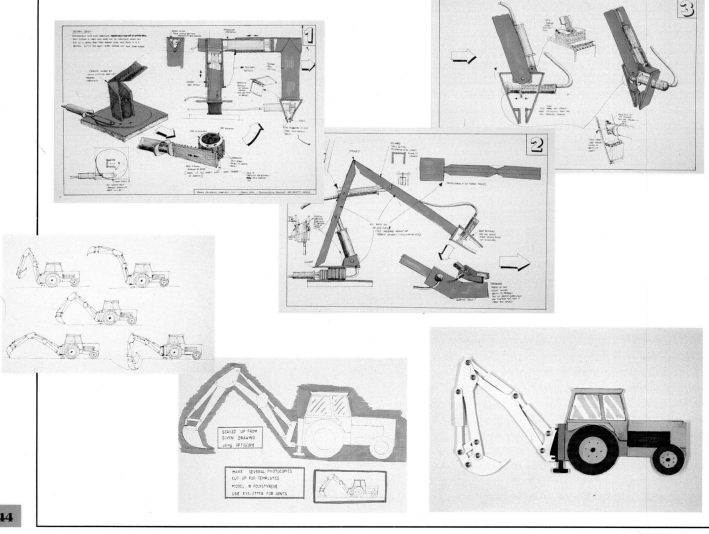

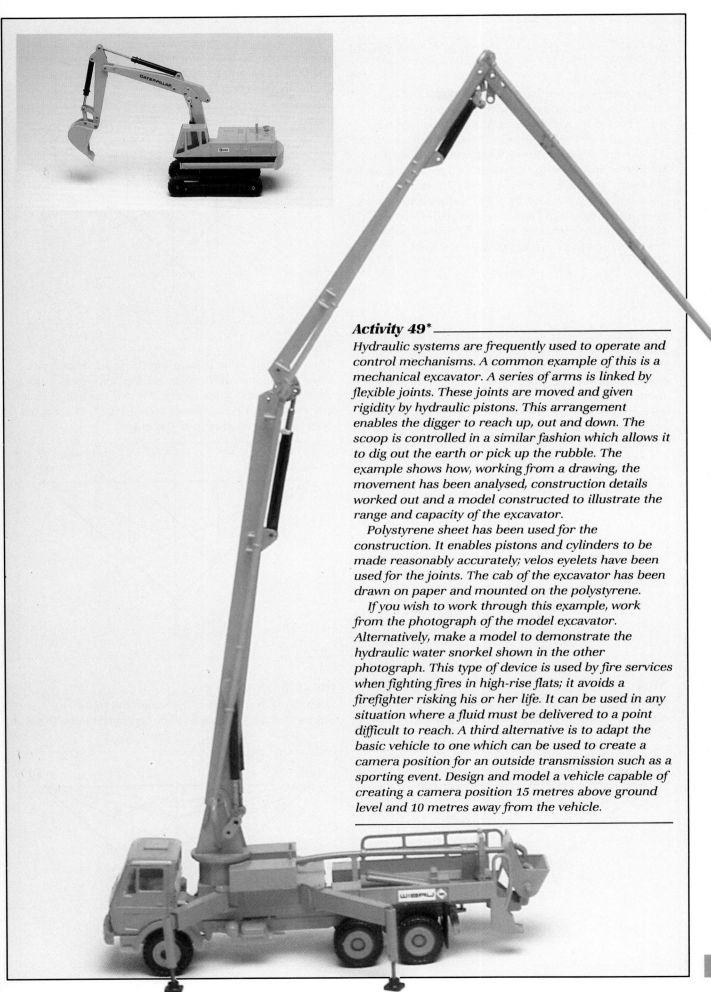

Activity 49*

Hydraulic systems are frequently used to operate and control mechanisms. A common example of this is a mechanical excavator. A series of arms is linked by flexible joints. These joints are moved and given rigidity by hydraulic pistons. This arrangement enables the digger to reach up, out and down. The scoop is controlled in a similar fashion which allows it to dig out the earth or pick up the rubble. The example shows how, working from a drawing, the movement has been analysed, construction details worked out and a model constructed to illustrate the range and capacity of the excavator.

Polystyrene sheet has been used for the construction. It enables pistons and cylinders to be made reasonably accurately; velos eyelets have been used for the joints. The cab of the excavator has been drawn on paper and mounted on the polystyrene.

If you wish to work through this example, work from the photograph of the model excavator. Alternatively, make a model to demonstrate the hydraulic water snorkel shown in the other photograph. This type of device is used by fire services when fighting fires in high-rise flats; it avoids a firefighter risking his or her life. It can be used in any situation where a fluid must be delivered to a point difficult to reach. A third alternative is to adapt the basic vehicle to one which can be used to create a camera position for an outside transmission such as a sporting event. Design and model a vehicle capable of creating a camera position 15 metres above ground level and 10 metres away from the vehicle.

PICTORIAL AND PRESENTATION DRAWING

Constructing grids

A grid can be a useful aid whether sketching or producing presentation drawings. A grid can be constructed in any drawing system. It can then be used as either a guide or an underlay to produce the framework of a more complex drawing. You are probably familiar with the construction and use of an isometric grid; the construction on this page will show you, step-by-step, how to produce a two-point perspective grid. This construction will show you how to construct a cube in perspective which can then become the starting point for the grid.

Stage 1

Draw a horizon line and establish two vanishing points VP1 and VP2. Bisect the distance between them to determine the sight line.

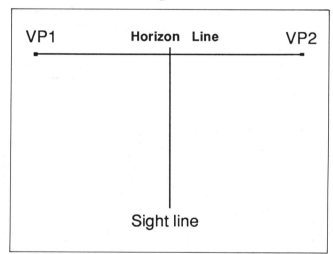

Stage 2

Draw two lines from each vanishing point which intersect on the sight line at points A and C. These lines establish the base of the cube ABCD.

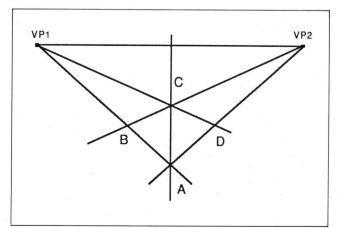

Stage 3

A section of the sight line will form the front edge of the cube. The other two edges can be projected up vertically from B and D.

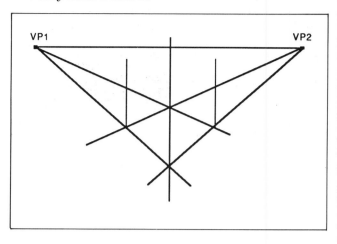

Stage 4

The top of the cube is found in the following way. Place a compass point on B, set the compass to the distance BD and draw an arc. Then draw a 45 degree line from point B to intersect the arc at E. Point E lies on a diagonal of the top of the cube.

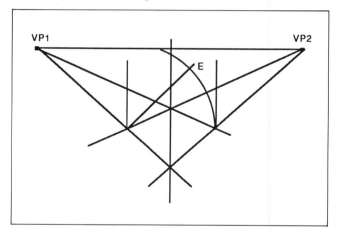

Stage 5

Draw lines from each of the vanishing points to points P and S to complete the top of the cube PQRS.

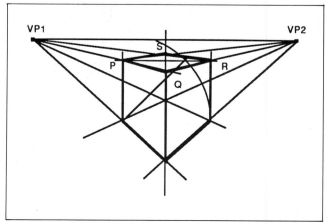

Stage 6

The faces of the cube can be divided up by first drawing in the diagonals and then adding a line from the vanishing point passing through the point where the diagonals intersect. This divides the original cube into eight cubes. Sub-divide each cube again and you have a 64 cube grid.

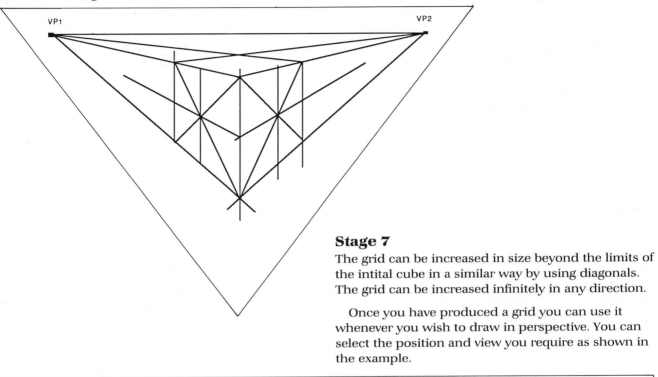

Stage 7

The grid can be increased in size beyond the limits of the intital cube in a similar way by using diagonals. The grid can be increased infinitely in any direction.

Once you have produced a grid you can use it whenever you wish to draw in perspective. You can select the position and view you require as shown in the example.

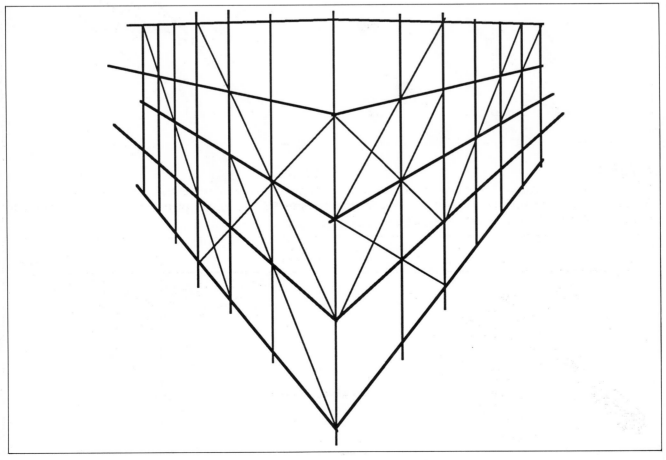

Examples

Although this unit deals mainly with the production of formal presentation drawings which tend to come towards the end of a design project, sketches and roughs can be good enough to be displayed. This page shows some examples of sketches relating to the design of a dustbug. Though only roughs done with ordinary pencils, they are well worthy of display as they illustrate how a designer's mind was working. They show how important it is to keep all your drawings.

The other drawings show the development sketches for the design of a pen to be made out of plastic tubing. These have been produced using felt markers. Simple projection systems — one-point perspective and orthographic projection — have been used, but as you can see the resulting drawings are very effective.

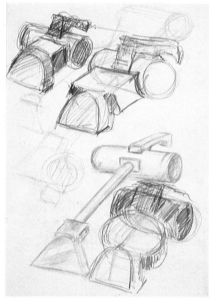
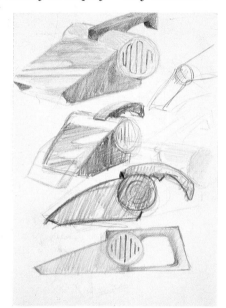
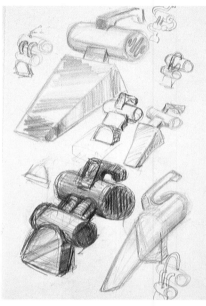

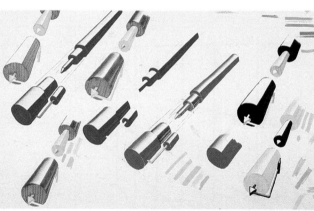
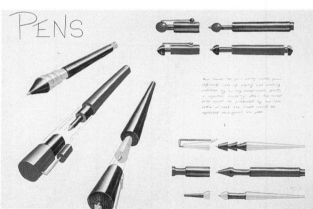

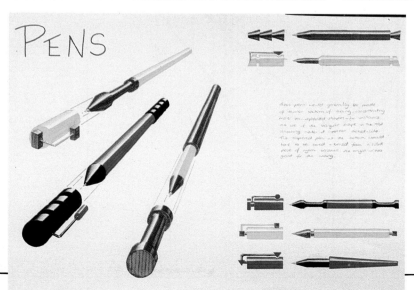

Activity 50*

Design, only to sketch stage, a wide range of solutions to either of the projects shown on this page — a dustbug or a ball point pen. Use colour wherever possible to improve the quality of your drawings. Try copying the techniques shown on this page.

Rendering details

Activity 51

Many consumer products are injection moulded, and as a result they share many similar visual elements: surface textures such as raised dimples and grooves, switches and buttons, break or moulding lines and grills. This page illustrates how these features, drawn orthographically, can be rendered to appear three-dimensional. Follow through the stages, then have a go at these drawings or similar ones yourself. The key point is identifying the direction of the light source. Thinking of the light source as coming from above a highlight on the top of the object always makes it appear to be upstanding from a surface. If you reverse this and put the hightlight at the bottom it will appear as a hollow.

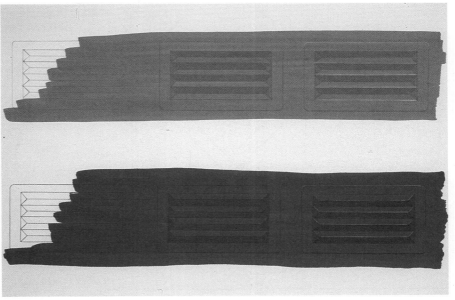

Isometric drawing

In many design situations it is necessary to draw and evaluate ideas in a pictorial three-dimensional form. There is a variety of systems which can be used. Certain types of designers prefer particular projection systems. Each system has advantages and disadvantages. You must be capable of selecting the most appropriate for the design situation with which you are involved.

Pictorial views are easily divided into two categories:

1 **Paraline drawings** — made up of parallel lines which take no account of foreshortening. These drawings can be produced quickly and easily with the use of set squares. Paraline drawings are governed by established rules. As a result two people drawing the same view of an object will produce identical drawings.

2 **Perspective drawings** — these take account of the easily observed fact that parallel lines converge to a vanishing point as they recede into the distance. They are more difficult to draw as certain elements of the construction are left to the designer to decide. As a result two people might produce different looking drawings of the same view of an object.

Here are a number of drawings of an audio cassette box drawn in a variety of projections. Which view is drawn in which projection? Which projection system has been used more than once?

It is not essential to be familiar with every projection system. There are four key ones on which you should concentrate your attention:

- **Isometric.**
- **Planometric/axonometric.**
- **One-point perspective.**
- **Two-point persepctive.**

Isometric projection

The rules of the projection are as follows:
- Lines which are vertical on the object will be vertical in the drawing.
- Lines which are horizontal on the object will be at 30 degrees to the horizontal in the drawing.
- All measurements on paralines are true (or all are scaled by the same amount if necessary).
- Circles will appear as ellipses.

There are no true shapes in isometric drawing. Because of this it is not very satisfactory for communicating sizes and measurements. Circles have to be constructed using a grid, (page 174). Alternatively, and far more accurately, use templates. Start by drawing, in isometric projection, the square in which the circle will fit and then use the template. The curve will touch the square at four points and these are used to align the template correctly. Remember, whenever you draw an object in a paraline projection, start by drawing the crate into which it will fit.

Activity 52

The cross-section of the proposed Channel Tunnel is shown below. Construct an isometric view of a section of the tunnel. Now use your drawing to design one of the following:

1 A promotional T-shirt.
2 A plastic bag for use in the Duty Free shop.
3 A baggage label.
4 A GB sticker indicating that the car crossed the channel using the tunnel.

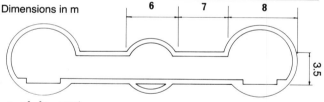

Dimensions in m   6   7   8   3.5

Activity 53*

Extrusion *is a process used to produce long lengths of a material with a uniform cross-section. The process involves forcing the material (commonly a metal or thermoplastic) through a hole or gap, normally called a **die**, to form a rod, ribbon, tube etc. The material flows plastically. It is the same process as icing a cake where different nozzles are used to produce contrasting shapes. The pressures and forces required to extrude metal are enormous. The most common metal to be extruded is aluminum and its family of alloys.*

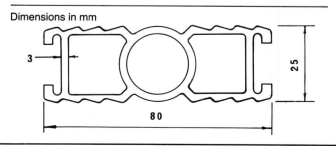

Dimensions in mm   3   25   80

EXTRUSION

TO DECORATE A CAKE WE USE A SYRINGE TO **EXTRUDE** LENGTHS OF ICING THROUGH A NOZZLE.

IN INDUSTRY PLASTICS, ALUMINIUM AND OTHER MATERIALS ARE SOFTENED AND FORCED THROUGH A '**DIE**'....

TYPICAL EXAMPLES ARE PLASTIC GUTTERS AND ALUMINIUM WINDOW FRAMES.

TO PRODUCE LONG LENGTHS OF A **SECTION**...

Curtain rails are a common example of plastic extrusion, as are guttering and hoses. UPVC window frames have been extruded — the process ensures dimensional accuracy. The cross-section shown is of an alumnium extrusion used for cycle pedals. It reduced the number of components in a pedal body from eight to two. Draw an isometric view of a 100 mm length of the extrusion, a length suitable for a pedal.

Look around and see how many other extrusions you can spot. Design an extrusion which will be suitable for one of the following situations, then draw the cross-section and make an isometric drawing of a length of the extrusion:

1 A length of tracking for sliding doors. The extrusion should be capable of being screwed to an overhead beam and of carrying two doors suspended on wheels. The doors should be able to slide past each other. The cross-section you design should be capable of scaling up or down so dimensions are not important, only proportions.

2 A flexible plastic extrusion suitable for providing an attractive edging on 25 mm manufactured board. You must determine how the lipping will be fixed to the board. Draw your solution twice full size.

3 A plastic version of tongue and groove boarding. When a design is transferred from one material to another with no changes being made, it is called a Chinese copy — they are rarely successful. You must return to the original brief and then see how it can best be solved in a plastic material. List the advantages that your extrusion will have over wood. Can you think of situations where it will be particularly useful?

Planometric drawing

The rules of **planometric** projection are as follows:

- The plan is true and drawn at an angle to the horizontal.
- All vertical edges remain vertical and are projected from the plan.
- All measurements are true (or all are scaled by the same amount if necessary).

Planometric or **axonometric** drawings, as they are frequently called by architects, are much quicker to construct than isometrics. The starting point is the plan view. The plan can be placed under a translucent material and traced prior to projecting the remainder of the object or building. Another advantage is that circles parallel to the plane of the plan can be drawn with a compass.

This projection is more flexible than isometric projection as the plan can be positioned at any angle to the horizontal. As a result, a range of slightly different views can be obtained. The view obtained from an axonometric projection forces the designer to look down. It is as if he or she is hovering above the subject. In the case of buildings, this view is seen only from aircraft. An architect should also produce views from street level of how the building will appear, as this is how it will normally be seen.

Activity 54

Blow moulding is a process used primarily to form plastic bottles. A tube of thermoplastic is pulled into a two-part mould. The mould parts come together so that the bottom of the tube is sealed and the top remains open. Air is then pumped into the tube which expands to fill the mould. The two parts of the mould open and the moulded bottle is ejected (see page 26).

The plastic bottle has been formed in this way. The

bottle has been drawn in axonometric projection. Working from either this drawing or from any other blow moulded bottle (choose one circular in cross-section), make an axonometric drawing of what you think the mould would look like.

The verbal description of how blow mouldings are produced is difficult to understand. Produce diagrams to accompany this text. It is most easily explained in four stages. Do the four drawings in axonometric projection.

Find out what PET stands for. What is special about this plastic? How has it revolutionized shopping habits? What has been the result?

Activity 55

Make an axonometric drawing of the house which you designed from the plan view in Activity 15. You will have to determine what an end elevation will look like in addition to the front elevation which you have already drawn.

Activity 56*

Working from a plan of your school site produce an axonometric drawing of the site. Heights of buildings may have to be estimated. This can be done quite accurately if the heights of individual floors are known. Design a front cover for the school magazine or handbook which incorporates your drawing.

Designers' examples

Gull Wing seating

Fitch and Company were responsible for the interior design of the new Terminal 4 at London's Heathrow Airport. This is a vast undertaking which includes every aspect, for example the check-in, baggage handling system, furnishings and furniture. The new terminal cost £200 million, covers 90 000 m² (one million ft²) and has been designed to handle 4000 passengers every hour, 8 million a year.

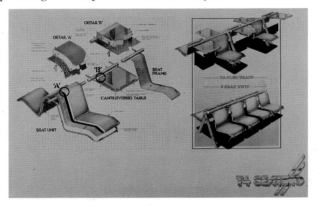

It was felt that no furniture existed which would meet the terminal's requirements, so Fitch embarked on an extensive design and development programme to create a range of new furniture. The most ambitious new design is the passenger seating, Gull Wing-Terminus, which is manufactured by Hille International.

The designer responsible for furniture design at Fitch, Paul Stead, has produced a flexible, ergonomically sound, economic and visually pleasing solution. The detail of the design can be understood from these rendered isometric drawings. They are excellent examples of how information about a product's construction can be conveyed using exploded and cut away views. These drawings dissect completely every aspect of the design.

Activity 57

At the time of this project the design manager at the British Airports Authority was Jane Priestman. She now has a similar post with British Rail. Imagine she had to write a brief relating to passenger seating at the airport's new terminal. Have a go at doing this job for her — write a concise brief outlining the functional and visual requirements of the seating. You are not in a postion to make any statements regarding the cost.

Activity 58

Prepare a fact sheet on one of the following architects: Richard Rogers, Norman Foster, Terry Farrell and James Stirling. Try to find out about some of the famous modern buildings they have designed, such as Centre Pompidou, Sainsbury Centre for the Arts, Stuttgart Museum and the TV AM building.

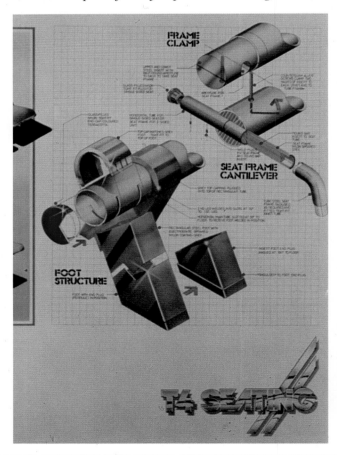

Lloyd's of London

The new Lloyd's building is one of the best examples of hi-tech architecture in the United Kingdom. The architects were Richard Rogers and Partners and the structural and service engineers were Ove Arrup and Partners. The building is very distinctive and created a great deal of controversy. It is set in the heart of the City of London and surrounded by narrow streets and tight winding alleys. Richard Rogers and Partners won a competition which attracted submissions from 40 architectural practices. The winning design team stated that their aim was to design and define a system or strategy, not a building.

Lloyd's of London dates back to the seventeenth century. It started in Edward Lloyd's coffee shop. It is now considered the centre of world insurance. Lloyd's is a society of insurance underwriters grouped in syndicates. It is like a market place; syndicates operate from stalls where they agree terms for accepting risks in whole or part. The efficiency of Lloyd's depends on a single market place, under one roof, known as The Room. The architects of the new building have created an underwriting room as a series of concentric galleries overlooking a central atrium. This flexible open space is capable of expansion and contraction as needs dictate.

All normal fixed obstructions such as lifts, stairs, toilets, entrances and columns are placed outside the building in six vertical columns. All aspects of the building requiring maintenance are located in these accessible towers, which are surmounted by cranes. The drawings on this page illustrate certain aspects of the building. The site plan shows clearly the central atrium and the six service towers. Notice how shadows have been added to create the illusion of different levels. The cross-section shows The Room on several levels connected by escalators, the barrelled atrium, and the towers with their service cranes. The colour-washed elevation gives a realistic view of the external elevations and the relationship between the new building and the portico of the previous building which has been incorporated.

The axonometric view illustrates the total concept of the building. You can see why it is such a useful system for both thinking ideas through and presenting concepts to clients.

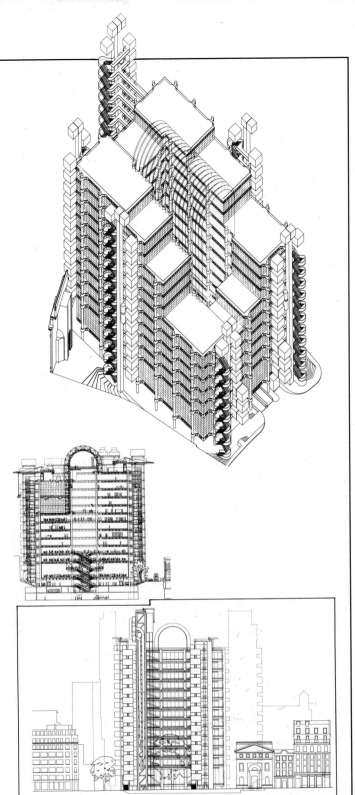

Activity 59*

Select a modern building in your area. Make some sketches of the building from different aspects. Try to draw a plan. What do you think the architect was trying to achieve? How does the building work or function? In your opinion, does it appear to succeed? Undertake a critical evaluation of the building. It will be subjective as you do not have access to all the information. Observe, record, question and evaluate. Architects are responsible for much of our living environment so you should learn to examine their ideas critically yet dispassionately.

Perspective drawing

Perspective drawings will vary according to the number of vanishing points selected. One-point perspective is good for interiors, two-point is used infrequently and generally only for large buildings. The majority of perspectives which you draw will be estimated. You will use your visual perception to judge the amount of foreshortening. The rules of perspective are as follows:

- Parallel lines converge towards a vanishing point where they disappear.
- Equal lengths foreshorten more the further they are from the vanishing point.
- In one-point perspective the surface closest to the viewing point is the only true one. All measurements must be taken on it.
- In two-point perspective the vertical edge closest to the viewing point is the only true one and all heights must be measured on it.
- If the view has more than one vanishing point, they will be positioned on the horizon line which is always horizontal.

Measured perspective

When you wish to produce a presentation drawing it is worth making a measured perspective. Often you will not calculate the position of everything precisely but it will help you establish correct proportions and the position of the key features.

Example

This page shows the stages in constructing a perspective of a Durabeam torch. Initially it will be drawn as a crate, equal in size to the maximum sizes of the torch. The detail will be added and then on the next page you will see the stages in rendering it. Detailed dimensions are shown in the orthographic views.

Stage 1

Use an A2 piece of paper. Start by drawing the plan view of the torch in the position shown. Add the line of vision and the horizon line. The line of vision is in the centre of the page and at right angles to the horizon line. The plan view is at 45 degrees to the horizon line.

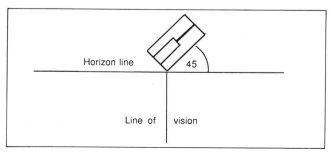

Stage 2

The next task is to establish the viewing point and the vanishing points. Measure the height of the object to be drawn (generally objects have to be scaled down). The viewing point should be a minimum of three and a maximum of five times the height at which the object is to be drawn. With experience you will learn to judge the best position. If in doubt place the viewing point further away than estimated. From the viewing point draw lines parallel to the edges of the plan view of the torch to establish the vanishing points.

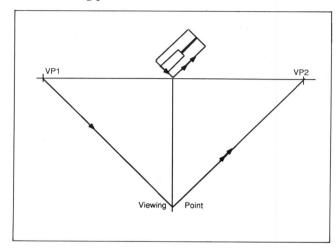

Stage 3

The front edge of the torch is now drawn on the line of vision. The distance from the bottom corner to the horizon line is equal to the height of the viewing point above the surface on which the torch is standing. Lines can then be drawn from the top and bottom of the front corner to the vanishing points.

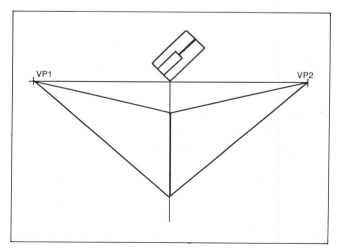

Stage 4

To determine the degree of foreshortening lines are drawn from the corners of the plan view towards the vanishing point as far as the horizon line. These lines are then taken down the paper parallel to the line of vision. They establish the front two faces of the crate. The back corner is found by projecting lines to the vanishing points.

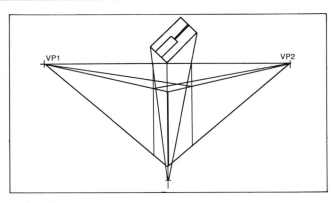

Stage 5

The remaining detail is added to the plan and then projected into the perspective view. The gap between the body and the rotating light source is determined by measuring on the front edge and joining to the vanishing point. The yellow spine of the torch is found by projecting from the plan view.

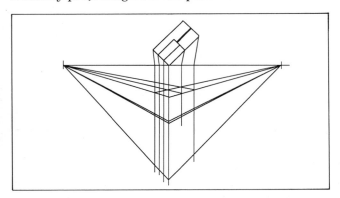

Modifying the view

A two-point perspective can be modified in two basic ways:

1 The plan view can be positioned at any angle to the horizon line. A 60/30 degree rotation is the other commonly used position. Remember that the lines drawn from the viewing point to establish the vanishing points must always be parallel to the edges of the plan view.

2 The front edge of the object can be moved relative to the horizon line. The horizon line can pass through the object or even below it. Remember that the plan must always touch the horizon line.

These two variables allow different views to be obtained emphasizing different features. These three views illustrate the point. The first was drawn with the plan view at 60/30, the second is the completed view from the above construction and the third has the horizon line passing through the object.

Activity 60

Produce a two-point measured perspective of the Durabeam torch or a similar one. Do not attempt to draw one which is too complex — choose one which has a basic block shape.

Stage 6

The final part of the construction concerns drawing the cylindrical parts. This is done by drawing an orthographic view of the circle enclosed in a square, then adding the diagonals. The enclosing shape is drawn in perspective and the points which fall on the circumference of the curve are plotted. The shape is drawn freehand, or if you have a set of templates use them to give a precise shape.

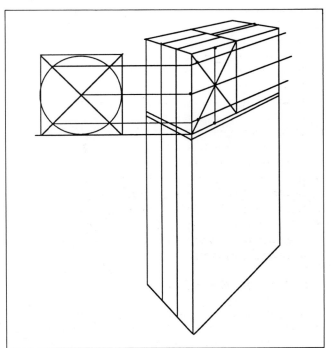

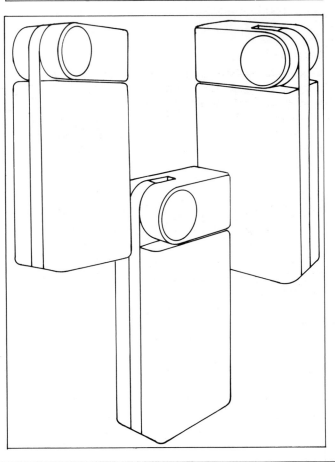

Rendering simple shapes

Before starting on a complex drawing, attempt to render some basic geometric shapes. Remember these are the building blocks of more complex shapes. Shown on this page are the stages in rendering a cuboid and a cylinder. Each shape is shown in three forms: glossy plastic, matt plastic and chrome.

Glossy plastic is very relective. Matt plastic is far less reflective and the light will only catch the corners and edges. Chrome is highly reflective and will only be realistically rendered if reflections of surrounding objects are shown.

In a cube consider each surface separately — one face will be dark, the other face a mid tone and the third the lightest. In a highly reflective material the top surface is best done using cotton wool and powdered pastel. Reflections can be added by removing pastel with an eraser. Highlights on the edges and corners are added to complete the view.

A cylinder is rendered by imagining it is positioned in an environment with no other objects and the sun or light source has just disappeared below the horizon. The result is that the reflection of the horizon will run along the axis of the cylinder. Below the line the cylinder will be dark as no light is falling on it. Above the line there will be an absence of colour, but the colour will gradually return as the cylinder curves back into shade. The top part of the cylinder is best rendered using powdered pastels.

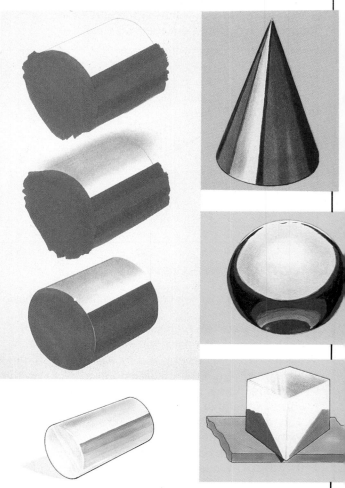

Activity 61

Attempt to render some basic geometric forms. Once you have mastered single units try putting them together to create more complex forms.

Activity 62

Produce a rendering of the torch drawn in Activity 60. If the torch is made up of two or more mouldings try a different colourway (colour combination) such as the red and grey Durabeam on this page.

Rendering a Durabeam torch

Once you have completed an outline the next step in producing a presentation drawing is to **render** it. This literally means to give a true representation, more simply stated as adding colour and texture to make the drawing as realistic as possible. As you become more competent you will develop your own style but begin by following these stages. As the torch is black plastic it is best rendered using markers. Use bleedproof paper to prevent solvents damaging the work surface or backing paper. If you are working on a photocopy take care as the marker solvent will cause the photocopy ink to bleed, causing discolouration. If this happens, make sure you clean the tip of the marker.

Stage 1
Make a copy of your completed drawing. Never work directly on your working drawing as it may well have construction lines etc. If your rendering goes wrong you can start again by producing another copy. If the object is black, as in this case, it can be drawn with a fine-line black pen. A general rule is to draw the object with a pencil the same colour as the object you are rendering. We automatically tend to draw in black (ink or graphite) but a yellow object has no black edges in reality. If our subject is very complex we may have to use a black outline to distinguish between the various parts.

Stage 2
Begin by using a broad-tip marker to block in all the black elements. At this stage ignore edges between black elements and the outline. Work quickly, maintaining a damp edge, this will help to prevent tide marks.

Stage 3
Next lay in the yellow components taking great care not to pull the black marker with the yellow one. Always lay in all the basic areas of flat colour first, allowing each marker to dry before going on to the next colour, and starting with the dark colours. The yellow plastic is bright and glossy unlike the body of the torch which is matt. The yellow components will be far more reflective. Notice how the top of the spine has been left white — it will be rendered as a cylinder.

Stage 4
A black marker is used around the edges to indicate the round corner, underneath the rotating element where it casts a shadow on the body, and for other elements where a darker tone will help bring out the form.

Stage 5
Detail can now be added. The front corner is defined using a white pencil. Edges which catch the light are rendered with a sharp white pencil. The curve of the yellow spine is completed using either a yellow pencil or pastel. The texture on the rotating part is drawn using a fine-line pen and a white coloured pencil.

Stage 6
Finally highlights are added either using a brush and gouache or a white fine-line pen. Do not add too many highlights, just place them on edges and corners which you think the light will strike directly. The raised lettering on the surface can be indicated by just the reflections.

Stage 7
Now the drawing can be cut out using a scalpel on a cutting mat. A clean sharp rendering is produced. The drawing can be mounted. A background helps make the drawing stand out from the page. Three different types are shown: a broken border; a backdrop produced with a marker — masking tape has been used to give sharp clean edges; and the use of a shadow to define the surface on which the torch is standing.

Car design

Designing a car is a highly complex task. The average car has over 7000 components, each the result of a designer or a team of designers producing the most suitable solution. This will involve designers from a wide range of disciplines — ergonomists, mechanical and electrical engineers, aerodynamic specialists and colour and fabric experts, for example. The coordination of the design team is crucial as they are just one element in the project. Market research, production engineering, promotion and advertising, retail and distribution are also vital if the new model is to appear in the showroom and appeal to the customer. The car industry is a highly competitive, international business — thousands of jobs depend on it as do the economies of many countries.

When we talk about cars we use many emotive words to describe how they look. As well as being interested in what goes on under the bonnet and a car's technical performance, it is the visual appearance which captures the imagination. One of the most important tasks in car design is using the shape and form of the car to project an image. The person responsible for this is the car stylist. This is a highly creative profession which requires an ability to draw and render complex shapes so that subtle changes in shape and form are apparent. Without these skills models would have to be made which are very expensive.

On these pages and the next two there are two examples for you to follow through. The first is the rendering of the body shell of a vehicle made in a school workshop. The shell is to be vacuum formed. The vehicle is battery driven and programmable — the project combines all aspects of CDT.

The second example is the work of a professional design team working for Ford. It is the design of a concept vehicle based on the Transit van. The Transit is a very flexible vehicle — there are many derivatives based on the cab and chassis. Your school minibus may be one of them — either the 9-, 12- or most likely the 15-seat version.

Vacuum formed bodyshell

Stage 1

This example is given to illustrate the stages in rendering. Initial sketches were used to explore the form. It is a good idea to start from orthographic sketches and develop ideas into three-dimensional forms. Once the form is determined, a rough rendering is produced to confirm the shape. In this case it is also important that the shell can be made by vacuum forming.

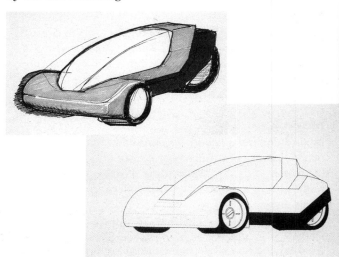

Stage 2

A line drawing is produced of all the essential elements. Rendering can now start. A black marker is used for the tyres. This is applied over the lines which indicate edges. A mid-grey is used for the skirt of the body — again no notice is taken of any detail.

The final stages of this rendering are shown in colour on page 60.

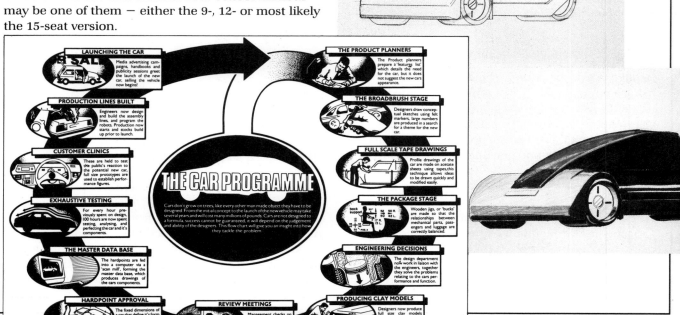

58

Transit

The designers of the Transit have produced a highly flexible unit which can be adapted for a variety of uses. Look at the six possibilities shown above — a van, a bus, a touring caravan, a panoramic view-roof extension, a box van, and a pick-up. These ideas were put together by the design team at Ford and described as 'thought starters'. You can see a range of rendering techniques. The most important tools for the car stylist are marker pens, coloured pencils and pastels. Cars are highly reflective objects. Glossy paintwork, and windows (called the greenhouse by designers), often appear almost colourless in bright light so a light brush of pastel is used to hint at the colour. Reflections are shown as stark simple images. Windows are often given a blue tint to indicate the reflection of the sky. The contours are often developed either by removing pastel with a clean eraser or using a white pencil on top of a surface coloured with a marker.

Activity 63

Design a bodyshell for a vehicle which could be vacuum formed. Remember if it is to be vacuum formed, it must be like a jelly mould so that the mould can be extracted. Once designed, produce a rendering of your vehicle by following the stages shown on this page and the next.

Activity 64*

Can you think of another use for a Transit? Using the line drawing of the cab and short wheelbase, add your purpose-built body and produce a rendering of your design. Alternatively complete the drawing in the bus form, then design a livery scheme and apply it. The livery scheme might be for your school minibus, a sports team or club you belong to or a community bus for your local bus company.

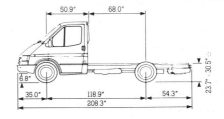

Activity 65*

Working from the internal plan of the Transit, design a suitable interior for a touring caravan capable of sleeping four people. Start by listing all the various requirements of such a vehicle. Then make a scale drawing of the given plan on grid paper. Make scale templates of the facilities you wish to incorporate. By moving them around on your plan explore possible layouts. You will have to work on a number of levels. It will be a good idea to produce a plan of the layout during the day and another showing the sleeping arrangements. Make a simple paper model to illustrate your design.

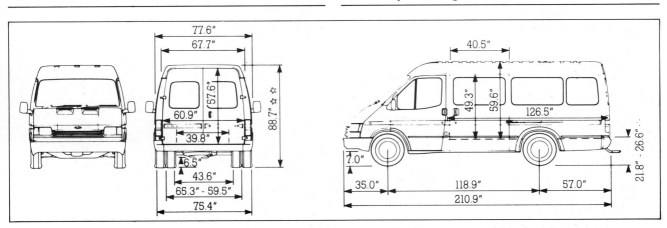

Stage 3

The main body of the vehicle is rendered with the chosen colour. Areas which will be in direct light and highly refelctive such as the bonnet are left blank at this stage. Once the marker has dried the drawing can be reworked. Darker areas such as under the body and behind the wheel arch are given a second application.

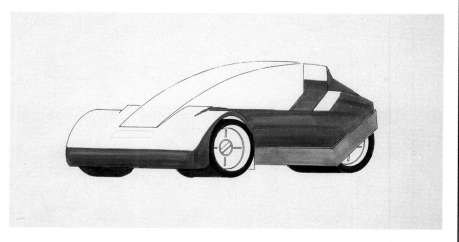

Stage 4

The area of the greenhouse not in direct light is rendered with a black and dark grey marker. The hubs are rendered using a mixture of blue and orange pastel and marker. White ink or gouache is used to redefine the edges of the tyres and to add some highlights.

Stage 5

Blue pastel is added to the bonnet and the remaining elements of the car in bright light. The pastel is scraped from the block using a scalpel and applied using cotton wool. Additional details can be added using colour pencils (see the panel on the bonnet).

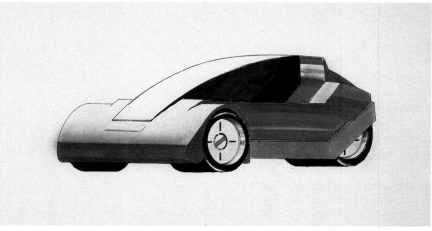

Stage 6

Now work can start on the background. This has been done using pastel and coloured pencil. Markers can be used but they can prove expensive when used on large areas. The basic streaks are orange pastel on to which some red has been added with a pencil. The required rectangle is cut out of the sheet and mounted on the final surface.

Stage 7

The body of the car is cut out ready for mounting on the backdrop. The remaining, unrendered element of the greenhouse is not included. The vehicle is mounted on the background. The edge of the greenhouse is indicated with white ink. It now appears as though you can see right through the cockpit. The backdrop under the vehicle is reworked with a black pencil and final highlights are added — the rendering is complete.

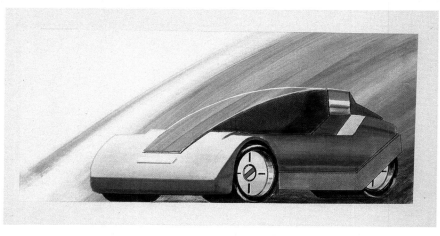

Chasseur

This derivative of the Transit was seen by the designers as a luxury vehicle with a number of novel features. It is equipped to a very high level. It is the kind of vehicle a group of business people might travel in whilst having a meeting or a pop group might use between gigs. It has leather upholstery, air conditioning, video display, telephones, advance sound system and computer links.

The exterior features overglazing (windows curving into the roof), an electric louvred sunroof, low body cladding (good for aerodynamics), front and rear airdams, alloy wheels and fast front body extension. The designers' drawings show how they thought the inside and outside might look. It was not just a designer's dream because as you can see in the photographs a fully working concept vehicle was built!

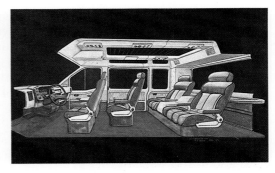

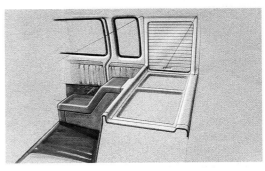

Exploded and cutaway drawings

When an orthographic view is sectioned it enables anyone with a trained eye to interpret from the drawing the internal arrangement of the object. Dotted lines which represent hidden detail are another method of showing internal construction. Section views and hidden detail are both generally used in orthographic two-dimensional drawings. The designer and illustrator frequently use exploded and cutaway drawings to give a more visual and easily understood view of an object or assembly. These types of drawings are nearly always pictorial projections, most commonly isometric and planometric and less frequently perspective. The drawings of the Gull Wing seating (page 52) show how well these types of drawings communicate ideas.

Exploded views stretch the space between the various pieces of an object in all directions. The designer or illustrator then freezes this explosion at the best point in time to show the relationship between the various parts. The drawing of the transit van illustrates this technique.

Exploded views are often used in manuals or instruction booklets to show how things go together, or indeed come apart. The instruction sheet shown here illustrates how a Slither Zoid is assembled. The first drawing is of the injection moulded components. A number of pieces are moulded in one go. You can see how the plastic flowed around the mould in channels. These channels narrowed to tiny sprues where the plastic entered the cavity in which each piece is formed. The pieces are easily disassembled by the purchaser, who can then make the zoid by following the instructions. This is an extremely cost effective method of manufacture and assembly, enabling the producer to keep the cost to a reasonable level.

These views are drawn in isometric projection. Notice how the individual parts are withdrawn along the axis of the space into which they fit. This is vital if the pieces are to look as if they will fit together.

Cutaway or peep-show graphics as they are sometimes called are used by all types of designers. An architect may remove part of the wall of a building to show the interior, or a furniture designer may remove parts of a chair to show the construction, as in the Gull Wing seating. The shell can be cut in one of three basic ways:

1 A cutaway which follows the external surfaces and appears logical and intended.
2 A jagged cut which pays no attention to the form of the drawing, giving a broken appearance.
3 A cut which contrasts strongly with the basic form, for example, a curvilinear cut in cuboid form.

Make sure the cut surface is clearly identified, otherwise it may cause confusion. A wide range of tones can be used as shown. Shading and line-hatching are effective as they allow the intensity to be varied. This can make the drawing appear more solid.

Illustrators frequently do drawings of complexity much larger than the final image required. This allows detail to be plotted accurately. The drawing is reduced photographically. If you have the facilities to do this, do a trial first to ensure the line thickness comes out correctly when reduced.

Use of self adhesive transfer tone

- First select the tone you feel to be most suitable. It may be an architectural pattern such as tiles or brick or a dot or hatched pattern.
- Place the sheet over the required area and with a sharp knife, such as a scalpel, cut a piece out of the sheet slightly larger than the area to be filled.
- Position the film carefully and smooth it down, taking care not to use too much pressure.
- Trim away the excess accurately to the required line.
- Cover the transfer with a clean sheet of paper and burnish it firmly.

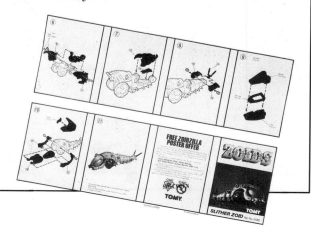

Follow these steps when doing an exploded drawing:

- Select the most important element which will be in the centre.
- Draw this in the chosen projection.
- Add the axis along which the other parts will move.
- Draw the crates into which the other parts will fit.
- Check that the distance of each from the main part is about the same.
- Add the detail in each crate.
- Using a light box trace the finished view on to a clean sheet or film.

The **cutaway drawing** of a gearbox is also drawn in isometric projection. It is a highly complex drawing but shows, with great clarity, exactly how the gearbox is assembled. Generally in a drawing of this type a quadrant of the outer casing is removed to reveal the internal workings. Drawings of this type frequently have to be reproduced in monotones so the illustrator has to create a range of tones and textures to enable the various surfaces to be distinguished.

A wide range of rub-down tones are available commercially. In this case a range of Letratones have been used. Some tones are rubbed on to the surface, coming away from the backing film. Others remain on the transparent film which is cut to fit the required space. Patterns can be overlaid to create individual effects, moire (watered) patterns and surface textures. Highlight effects can be created by removing the printed pattern using a scalpel, an ink eraser, white paint or correcting fluid.

Commercially the final piece of artwork would be a PMT (a photo mechanical transfer print). This is produced using a process camera. Any retouching or alterations will not show and the uneven surface created by the layers of film will disappear. A process camera will produce a perfect sharp image. Similar processes can be carried out using a photocopier, but the clarity and accuracy will not be comparable.

When producing a cutaway drawing follow these steps:

- Construct the complete assembly.
- Then decide on the section of the casing or skin to be removed.
- Draw in the cutting planes.
- Add the internal detail which has now been exposed.
- Once all the detail has been added, trace the drawing through on to a clean sheet of paper or film using a light box.

Activity 66

Select an item of furniture and produce an exploded view to illustrate clearly the construction. You may, for example, choose a chair, a table or a wardrobe; make sure you start by selecting an appropriate scale for your drawing. Show clearly the method employed to join the various pieces together. Annotate the finished drawing with constructional details and information on the materials used. This might be best done on a transparent overlay.

Activity 67*

Assess the storage requirements of a design and communication studio. All these resources have to be accommodated in a room 2.5 m by 3.0 m which is 2.75 m high. Produce a cutaway drawing to show how this room might be fitted out to meet the storage needs you have identified.

Activity 68

Produce an exploded view of one of the following: a radiator valve, a torch, a pen, a mouse (computer peripheral), a soldering iron, a lock or a scent bottle atomizer.

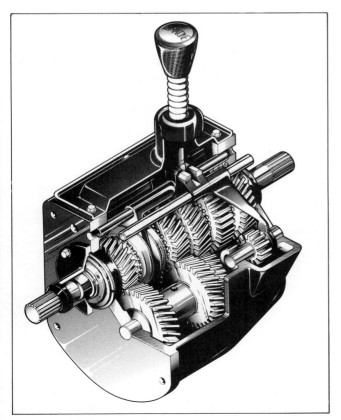

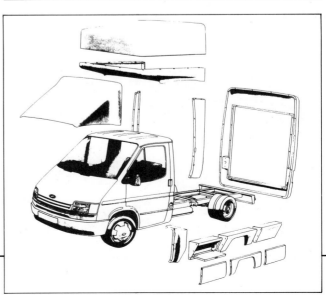

SEMIOLOGY AND INFORMATION GRAPHICS

Diagrams

Diagrams are used to organize our ideas and experiences. They simplify our world and make it more intelligible. Many diagrams have special names. Geographers produce diagrams which deal with the spatial arrangement of both the natural and manufactured world; we call them **maps**. **Charts** and **graphs** are specialized diagrams used by statisticians and critical path analysis is used by people who plan and organize. Engineers use diagrams to communicate ideas, for example, **circuit diagrams** in electronics.

The British Standards Institute publishes guidelines on the making of diagrams and the symbols which should be used for particular ones. It is important that everyone conforms to these standards so that there is a common language. The BSI publishes a booklet with examples of these symbols specifically for schools (PP 7307). Ask your teacher, the school will almost certainly have copies.

Maps

Most maps have symbols which are used instead of words. You are probably familiar with Ordnance Survey maps and the symbols which they use. They are always described in the key or legend. Most maps reflect the world as it really is. The map is an accurately scaled down representation. Perception maps distort reality as an aid to getting the information across more effectively. The most famous example is the London Underground map designed by Harry Beck. He enlarged the central area with its concentration of stations and reduced suburban areas where the distance between stations was much greater. He also straightened out routes, distorting the relative locations of stations. For most people the Underground map has become their perception of London.

Every map has a specific purpose and the person designing a map must make that the priority and remove the unwanted information. Cartographers may distort the size of countries in relation to their population or some other factor being compared. A map of the InterCity rail network would only show major stations and the distance between stations may be determined according to travel times rather than the actual distance.

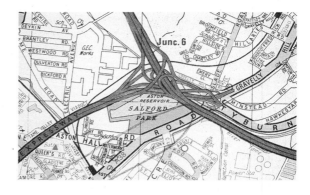

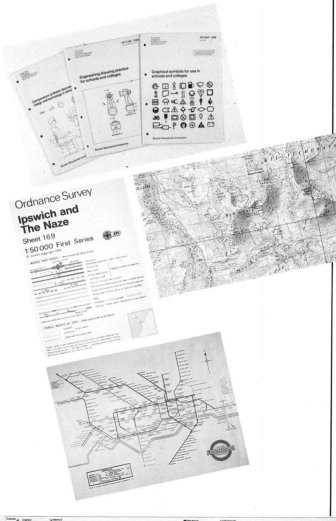

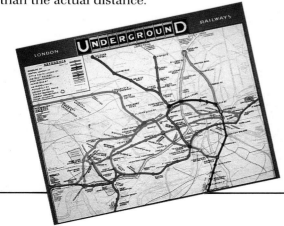

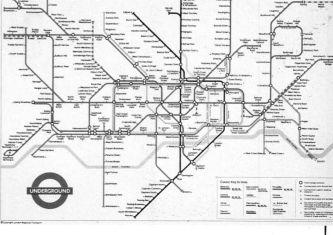

Flow diagrams

A **flow diagram** is one that shows movement. It might be the flow path of people through an exhibition or cafeteria, a one-way traffic system or a family or genealogical tree. It might also be used to show stages in making or producing something or the way in which a problem might be tackled. Another use is to show repetitive operations on a plan as an aid to redesigning the layout more efficiently.

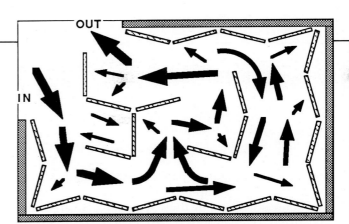

Sequence diagrams

A **sequence diagram** is used to show how something should be done. It will show visually the various stages in the correct order. They are frequently found with kits and products which need assembling such as flat-pack furniture. A good diagram will show the information clearly. This means carefully deciding what information is required and the number of stages which are involved. The diagram must then show these stages in the correct order. Objects are generally simplified to line drawings to focus attention, however photographs are sometimes used as in car repair manuals.

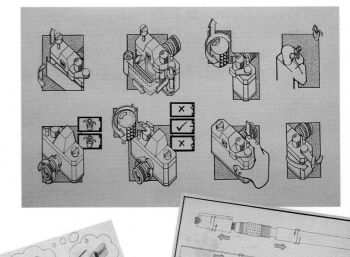

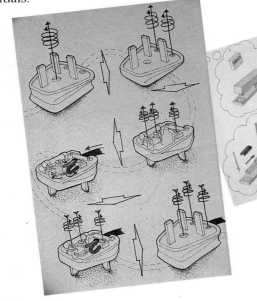

Activity 69*

Choose a local civic amenity, such as a museum, theatre, sports complex or shopping centre and produce an aid which would show how to get there by all the available forms of transport. The final piece of graphics should fit on a postcard.

Activity 70

Produce a sequence diagram which will help a person to carry out one of the following operations:
- Making jam.
- Mending a punctured bicycle tyre.
- Applying make-up to the face.
- Pruning a rose bush.

Activity 71

Investigate carefully and then produce a flow diagram to show one of the following:
- The decoration of a room in your home.
- The movements of one player in a team game such as hockey, rugby or basketball.
- The strokes played in a game such as cricket or tennis by a player.
- The educational options open to someone on completion of their GCSE examinations.

Activity 72

Investigate perception maps similar to the London Underground map. Design a perception map based on your local bus services.

Corporate identity

Nearly everybody identifies with particular groups of people. It might be because they all support the same football team, like the same pop group or dress in a similar way. Any group of people with the same interest develops similar patterns of behaviour, ideas and ambitions. A group is said to have **characteristics**, and by these its members can be recognized. Often groups wear badges or uniforms so that they can be easily identified.

Large companies are very concerned about their **corporate identity** or reputation. Every company or organization wishes to be well thought of by those on the inside such as its staff, and those on the outside such as its customers. Corporate identity is often thought of as the visual character of a company, but in reality it is much more than that. It can help to make a company more efficient and competitive and as a result, improve profits.

Design consultancies specialize in corporate identity work. A company's **trademark** or **logo** is the most visible result of its work. A consultancy will produce a manual which will control every visual aspect of the company from letter heads to shopfronts; all aspects will be uniform to help create a strong corporate identity.

Trademarks

These are the essential elements around which a company's visual character is built. There are many with which you are very familiar. A trademark is a shorthand symbol which stands for the company. Some have evolved, such as the AEG logotype shown here, and others have been designed, such as the Body Shop trademark. The AEG logos were designed between 1896 and 1912. The final one was designed by Peter Behrens and is still in use today.

Trademarks fall into four categories:
- Symbolic — often a graphical image which has something to do with either the name of the company or its product.
- Abstract — an image which may say something about the company's attitudes or may have been developed from its name or initials.
- Written — a stylized drawing of the company's name or initials, or it might even be based on the founder's signature.
- Pictorial — a picture which relates to the company's name or product.

Activity 73 – Research

Collect a number of company trademarks. Analyse each in terms of the categories given. Comment on how successful you think each is. Select ten and carry out a piece of market research to discover the recognition rating of each of the logotypes. You will need to survey a minimum of twenty people. Present your findings visually using one of the techniques outlined earlier in this section. Visual impact is important, but remember your results should still be easily interpreted.

Activity 74

Trademarks are often designed around the initial letter of a company's name. A is frequently used, as in the examples shown. The design sheet below shows some possible trademarks for six imaginary companies all beginning with the letter A. They are mainly symbolic solutions. Try designing trademarks for five of these companies based on the initial letter B:

Bicycle, Business, Babyneeds, Bionic Robots, Bistro Eiffel, Bolt Security, Bookworm, Bridge Credit, Burgers Supreme, Beacon Communication, Bikini Boutique

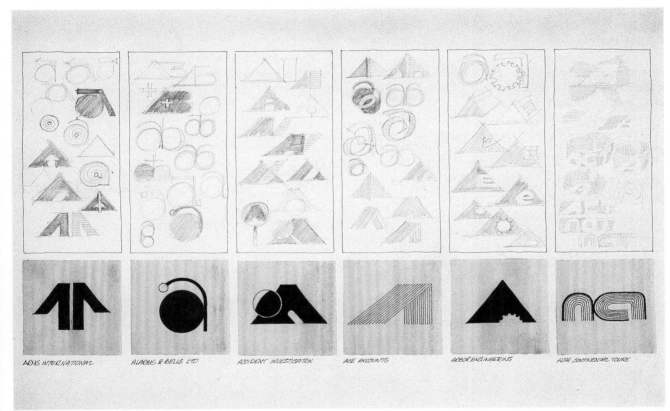

ARMS INTERNATIONAL   ALARMS & BELLS LTD   ACCIDENT INVESTIGATION   ACE ACCOUNTS   ARBOR ENGINEERING   ALFA CONTINENTAL TOURS

Activity 75

A trademark must be able to be drawn accurately and precisely every time. Consequently it must be able to be drawn geometrically. Have a look at the Body Shop trademark. It can be drawn entirely with a compass. See if you can draw it from the information you have been given. Now select the best solution in your opinion to a trademark based on a letter B, and translate it into a geometric drawing. Measurements are usually given in relation to an X value so that the trademark can easily be redrawn at any scale. Dimension your drawing in this way; the smallest dimension will be X and all others multiples of it.

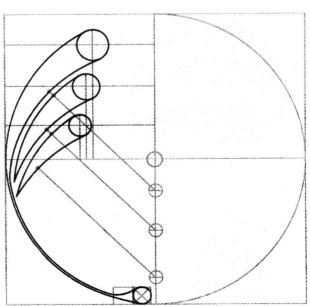

The Body Shop

A corporate identity programme

When a company embarks on implementing a corporate identity programme the design team will be responsible for reviewing all the company's visual elements. This will include the company and brand names, corporate symbols, trademark, colourways and type faces. These must be considered in relation to all the following aspects:

- Corporate papers.
- Vehicle identification.
- Product design.
- Signs.
- Uniform.
- Packaging design.
- Advertising.
- Exhibitions.
- Sales promotional material.
- Environmental design.

Case study – the Body Shop

The Body Shop was founded in the mid-seventies by Anita Roddick. As its name implies, it sells products to do with body care: shampoos, soaps, suntan oil etc. There is probably a Body Shop in your local shopping centre. When Anita started the venture the products were made up on the kitchen table and sold through a single outlet in Brighton. Products were supplied in simple, economic yet efficient containers in five standard sizes. An image born out of common sense established an identity which fitted perfectly the Body Shop products: natural treatments and cosmetics at reasonable prices.

The financial limitations of the venture helped establish the successful formula,

We couldn't afford a big shop, so we had a little one. It had damp walls so we painted them bright green. We could only afford a few products, so we made them look more by doing different sizes. We couldn't afford many bottles so we inauguarated the refill system. We couldn't afford fancy packaging, so we did hand-written labels... The Body Shop is also unique; we do not encourage false images of beauty and claims of youth. We create products that cleanse, polish and protect skin and hair using natural, healthy ingredients sold in environments that are sensual theatre, pure and simple.

Anita Roddick

The Body Shop is now a multi-million pound organization with over 315 outlets in 33 countries as far flung as Canada, Australia, Singapore, Dubai and, of course, over 98 outlets in the UK.

Only six of the Body Shops are owned by the company, the majority are **franchised**. A franchise is an agreement between the parent company and a subsidiary to sell the company's goods or services at a specific outlet or in a particular area. The agreement will have many conditions, such as the shop should only sell the principal company's products, or it must observe and maintain the corporate image established by the company.

The Body Shop has a specific image and reputation which Anita Roddick believes is essential to its success. To ensure that the rapidly expanding network of franchised operators maintained this house style she took advice from a consultancy specializing in corporate identity, The Yellow Pencil. The designers at The Yellow Pencil, led by Andy Ewan, started by producing a design manual. The manual had to encapsulate the spirit of the Body Shop whilst laying down guidelines about every aspect of the company's image.

Andy's team started by sharpening and updating the logo with which you are already familiar. They then set about defining how it should be related to signs, packaging, and printed material. Every possibility was examined and comprehensive details were given in the manual in the prescribed colourway of dark green and daffodil yellow. Now any new franchise can follow the instructions given in the manual ensuring that the Body Shop image will be identical from Singapore to Switzerland. The examples given here show details of the Body Shop sign, letterheads, shop fronts and products.

The Yellow Pencil are also responsible for shop window displays and packaging products. As it is impossible to hire window display artists for small outlets worldwide, silk-screened blinds are used. These are larger versions of promotional literature and are the responsibility of Andy's team. He often employs illustrators whose work seems to be in sympathy with the Body Shop image, several examples are shown.

Critical path analysis

In industry or commerce, when a production system has to be established, the production manager will frequently use a **network diagram**. This forces the manager to consider every aspect of an operation and ensure that nothing is left to chance. A particular type of network analysis is **critical path analysis**. This determines the shortest time span in which production can be achieved ensuring nothing is left out. This type of analysis may be useful when you have to start your major project. It should help you to establish deadlines by which certain phases of your project should be complete. This page describes in simple terms what can be a highly complex diagnostic tool.

The easiest way to explain critical path analysis is to work through an example. Our example will be to examine how I organize my time between getting up and going to work.

Stage 1 — Defining the task

Every operation or activity has a beginning and an end. These are represented by circles called **nodes** or **events**. They are particular points in time. In my case the start is getting up and the finish is going to work. At the moment these two events are jointed by a single arrow. The arrow represents an **activity**, in this example getting ready to go to work. The task is to produce a network diagram which shows all the various things which I must do if I am to leave for work on time.

Stage 2 — Analysing the task

The next step is to list all the various things I must do, and the time it takes to do them:

1 Take a shower 5 min.
2 Dry myself 3 min.
3 Shave 4 min.
4 Get dressed 4 min.
5 Clean my teeth 2 min.
6 Make the tea 3 min.
7 Make breakfast 4 min.
8 Feed the cat 1 min.
9 Eat breakfast 5 min.
10 Check diary 2 min.
11 Pack bag 3 min.
12 Say goodbye 2 min.

In total this is 12 activities taking 38 minutes. I have to get ready in 30 minutes so let us see if a network diagram can reveal how I manage it!

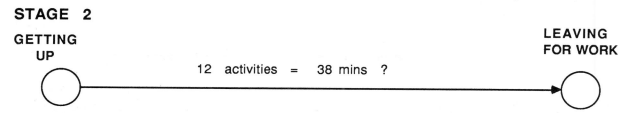

Stage 3 — Drawing the network

Now I can draw the network diagram consisting of a sequence of arrows (activities) and circles (events) which precisely define the task. The sequence of events should progress from left to right. The events are numbered so that the event at the tail of the arrow has a lower number than the event at the head. If an activity cannot start until two earlier activites have both been completed it is drawn as shown.

Sometimes it is necessary to use **dummy activity lines**. These are activities of zero time duration but are necessary to define a sequence of activities. For example, I know that the cat will not allow me to eat my breakfast until he has been fed. As a result the activity of the cat being fed is linked to my eating breakfast by a dummy line showing that I cannot start eating my breakfast until the activity of feeding the cat has been completed.

At the top of the page opposite is my network diagram with the activities on the arrows (AoA).

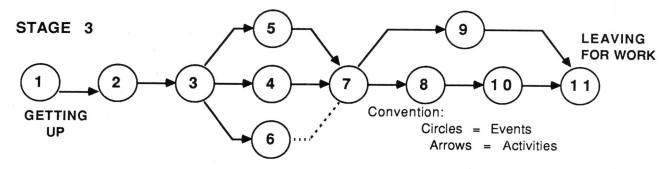

STAGE 4

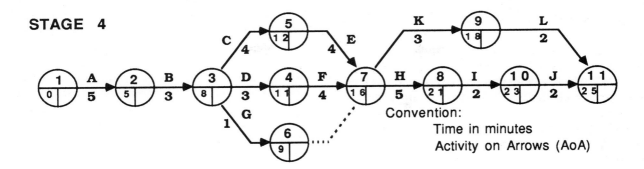

Convention:
Time in minutes
Activity on Arrows (AoA)

Stage 4 — Event times

Event 1 occurs at time zero. The times of the other events can be found by following the arrows and summing the activity times. Events can be reached in different times depending on how they are approached through the network. The earliest completion time must be the longest time path. Our events have now been divided into three parts. The number in the semicircle is the event number. The number in the bottom left quadrant is the time of the event. Event 7 is one which could be reached by more than one route. It is the longest time path via activities c and e which determines event time.

Stage 5 — The critical path

There is a path through the network on which any delay will immediately lengthen the completion time. This is called the **critical path**. It is found by working back against the arrows so that the latest finishing time for each event is established. These are shown in the bottom right quadrant. These latest finishing times are taken by subtracting activity times from the total project time, always taking the longest possible path time. For example, I can feed the cat any time between 9 and 16 minutes after getting up and it will not upset my schedule. If, though, I take more than two minutes to say goodbye to the family my critical path and completion time will increase and I shall be late. If I need to save time it is the critical path which must be investigated.

STAGE 5

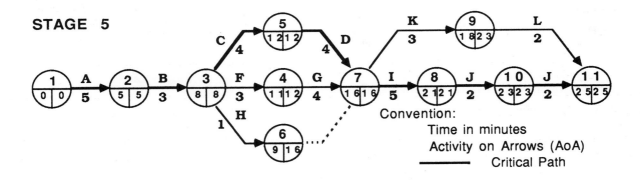

Convention:
Time in minutes
Activity on Arrows (AoA)
———— Critical Path

Conclusion

If all the activities took place sequentially it would take 38 minutes, but because I am capable of doing more than one thing at a time, theoretically I can save 13 minutes (more time in bed!). However, I am not superhuman and although I can shave (with an electric cordless razor) at the same time as making tea, I do not think I can do three things at once! In reality it takes about 30 minutes — but I'm working on it!

Network diagrams are very useful in establishing the logic of a project. In the shipbuilding industry everything was once geared around launch day. The installation of the plumbing and electricity had to be completed in advance of the launch. From network analysis they realized this was not the case. Launch the boat as soon as possible — this will only result in one day's delay in fitting out, which can then be completed at a different location — aboard the floating boat. Launch day becomes a minor event. Try using this approach on your major project. It should help you establish priorities in making sure you get finished on time.

Signs and symbols

Every day we all depend upon the ability to interpret a range of complex **signs** and **symbols**. The most obvious are traffic signs, but there is also a range of symbols used on control systems — central heating, photocopiers and remote controls for television, for example. Many of these symbols are ones which are part of our past and have been used since people first started using visual communication. The arrow is one such symbol which we all follow unhesitatingly. The symbols which we use in everyday life must leave no room for different interpretation, otherwise accidents would result. The first requirement of any sign or symbol is that its message is understood.

A language of pictures, or symbols, was first used by the cave dwellers of 50 000 years ago. All ancient civilizations developed their own sign system, such as Egyptian hieroglyphics. Gradually picture writing was replaced by phonetic writing. Symbols no longer represented real objects but words and sounds, an abstract system which could be adapted to describe anything. There are now over 100 languages in use with thousands of regional dialects — communication is more complex than ever!

Perhaps it is the complexity of language which has led to more and more signs and symbols in an attempt to make communication more direct. A symbol stands for something, it is a simplification which captures the essence of an object, operation or instruction. In a famous book called *Symbol Sourcebook*, Henry Dreyfus divided symbols into three areas:

- Representational symbols — accurate yet simplified pictures of objects or actions.
- Abstract symbols — the essential elements of a message are reduced to a graphic statement.
- Arbitrary symbols — an invented symbol which must be learnt.

Here are some symbols. What do you think they represent? Compare your answers with your friends.

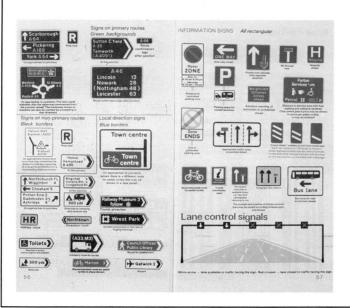

Colour is often used to improve the performance of a symbol. Red is used to indicate danger or stop, whilst green is used to indicate the opposite — start or go, as in traffic lights. In the United Kingdom the British Standards Institute produces guidelines and recommendations on all types of signs and symbols. For safety signs specific colours are defined. Red is used for prohibition signs, black and yellow for danger and warning signs, blue for mandatory signs and green for signs concerning safety.

Symbols, by their very nature, are composed of simple geometric shapes, squares, triangles, circles, diamonds etc. and combinations of these shapes. Often it is the simple nature of a design which makes it open to interpretation. The symbols whose meaning you were asked to suggest were produced for no particular purpose — they are just random images, but no doubt you imagined that they stood for something! Symbols are in 99 per cent of examples two-dimensional. If they were three-dimensional they would be even more likely to be misinterpreted.

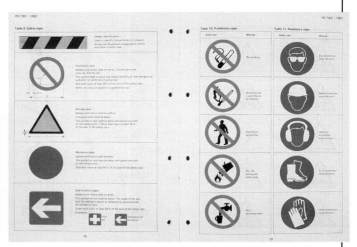

Activity 76* — Research

Find out as much as you can about the history of signs and symbols. Investigate watermarks, merchants' and masons' marks, branding and hallmarks for example. From your investigation produce a poster called 'Making sense of symbols'.

Record for one 24-hour period all the symbols which you use or come into contact with. Include everything from those on the clothes you wear to symbols on maps or in public places which help you find your way.

Activity 77

Design, in black and white only, symbols for the following opposites:
hot/cold, dark/light, heavy/light, empty/full, fast/slow
Try your symbols on your friends, then, in the light of their comments, try to improve on your designs.

Activity 78

Design symbols for each of one of the following groups:
- *The continents — Africa, Asia, Europe etc.*
- *Employees in the National Health Surface — doctors, dentists, nurses etc.*
- *Subjects in the National Curriculum.*

Activity 79

Symbols are used at large events such as the Olympic games. Look at the seven examples of symbols used to represent swimming. The first was for the 1948 games in London, and the last for the 1984 games in Los Angeles. Graphic styles have changed. In 1948 the symbol was like the heraldic badge worn on tracksuits, but by 1984 it had become almost an abstract pictogram. In 1992 the games will be held in Barcelona. Imagine that the following sports will be introduced for the first time and design symbols for them:

cricket, American football, squash, golf

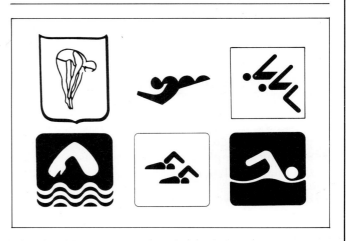

Designing surveys and questionnaires

It is very difficult to design in a vacuum. The more information you have about a brief or problem the better are your chances of coming up with a satisfactory solution. Often the facts you need have already been collected and you can find the answers in a reference book, such as a British Standards Institute publication. On other occasions you will need to carry out some research. Research may involve writing letters to manufacturers, designing test rigs, carrying out a product analysis or market research. Professional designers often employ market researchers to discover what are the real needs and requirements of the potential customer. You need to understand the techniques which they employ as you will have to do your own market research.

In simple terms market research involves asking those who might use the product or service questions about their needs, and then analysing the answers. The analysis will reveal **trends** — majority views about the topic being investigated. This gives the designer a clear indication of how to approach a project and some parameters against which solutions can be tested. Market research is carried out by either interviewing or using questionnaires. Each method has advantages and disadvantages. When conducting an interview the person being interviewed may well feel compromised and not give completely honest answers. On the other hand, response to a questionnaire is often poor. It is always important to try to obtain a random sample. It would be silly to carry out a survey about the football team which people support at Anfield (Liverpool's home ground) or any other ground because the answers would be biased.

A survey generally has the following characteristics:
- To produce statistics — a numerical description of an aspect of the population being studied.
- The main way of collecting information is by asking questions; the answers will form the data to be analysed.
- It is only possible to collect information from a fraction of the population, known as the **sample**.

Stages in carrying out a survey

A survey consists of three important elements:
- Designing the questions to make sure you find out what you want to know.
- Designing the questionnaire or interview so that it can be answered consistently.
- Selecting a sample which will be representative of the total population.

Designing questions

A question should be precisely worded and should mean the same to everyone being asked. It should be able to be answered simply and precisely. You will probably ask questions which will result in three types of information or data.

1. **Nominal data** A common method of answering a question is to ask the respondents (the people answering the question) to fit themselves or their experiences into a category. This is known as **nominal data**, for example, 'Are you male or female?', 'Do you own a bike?', 'Do you wear glasses?'. These types of questions sort people into ordered categories.

2. **Ratio data** Questions which result in a number that is a measurement on a precise physical scale produce **ratio data**. Some examples of this type of question might be, 'How old were you on your last birthday?' 'How much pocket money do you get?', or 'How many GCSE examinations are you taking?'.

3. **Ordinal data** If a question asks people to fit themselves into an ordered category, **ordinal data** will result. This is easy to understand from the example, 'How would you rate the amount of pocket money you receive — generous, adequate or insufficient?'.

An ordinal question can produce as many categories as the survey designer thinks necessary. For example, the question about pocket money could have been asked with just two possible responses, such as sufficient or insufficient. Or there might have been five possible answers.

These questions are the most difficult to design. If there were only two possible responses, probably many more would think their pocket money insufficient than if there were five possible responses. The normal response categories are as follows:
- Two-category scale   good, bad.
- Three-category scale   good, fair, poor.
- Four-category scale   very good, good, fair, poor.
- Five-category scale   excellent, very good, good, fair, poor.

Types of questions

Questions can be sub-divided into roughly two types, **open** and **closed**.
'What games do you play?' is an open question. 'Which of the following games do you play? hockey, netball, football or rugby' is a closed question.

Closed questions will produce data which is simpler to analyse but open questions could produce unanticipated answers which are very revealing.

Design and layout of a questionnaire

The first thing to decide is will the questionnaire be carried out by interview or will it be self-administered? In either case the wording should be precise and accurate, easy to understand and not open to a range of interpretations. Questionnaires which are to be self administered should be restricted to closed answers and the questions should have a similar pattern to them to avoid confusion.

Often questionnaires have skip patterns, for example, 'If your answer to question 5 was yes move to question 7, if your answer was no, answer question 6.' Good graphics and the use of arrows and boxes can help respondents to follow the questions they should answer.

The use of different typefaces for questions and answers can help to make a form visually more interesting and easy to answer. Do not crowd questions on to a page. A cluttered page generally slows down response rate and causes difficulties.

Remember, always pretest a questionnaire: get friends and teachers to try it out. Listen to their comments and modify the form to take account of their views. Try retrieving the information from the forms they have completed. Make sure your task after conducting the survey will be as straightforward as possible.

Sampling

It is important, if the results of your survey are to be useful in your design project, that you think carefully about who you will ask to answer it. This example will illustrate some of the issues.

If you were interested in what people thought of your local bus service it might seem obvious to ask those waiting at bus stops to complete your questionnaire. This would not be a random survey. You have selected a specific sample — bus users. Their views might be very useful in matching the service to the customers' needs but it would not, for example, tell you why people do not use the buses. A

self administered postal survey of 10 per cent of households living in a particular area would produce a selected sample. Alternatively an interview questionnaire carried out in a shopping centre would be a random survey. Each would produce different results. The postal survey would include only those living in the targeted area, whereas the shopping centre survey could include anyone who just happened to be there, including tourists or people involved in commercial activities.

Before you start asking the questions you must be certain why you are asking them. Do you want to improve the bus service for those who already use it, do you want to attract more users, or are you trying to establish that cuts can be made due to underuse of the service?

Activity 80

Carry out this activity in a small group of three or four. Tackle either one activity from A or one from B.

A Design a self administered questionnaire to investigate one of the following:

1 The perception of the school catering service by the school population.

2 A survey of your parents to investigate their television viewing habits.

B Design an interview questionnaire to investigate one of the following:

1 A survey of 14- to 16-year-olds to investigate their leisure time.

2 An investigation of the reading habits of your teachers.

Produce a report based on the results of your survey.

Statistical information

Statistics is all about figures or numerical information. It is the science of collecting, classifying and displaying quantifiable facts. Statistics have to be interpreted or analysed. There is no value in collecting data or statistics if nothing of value is learnt from them. You are probably familiar with looking at charts and graphs in mathematics, geography and other subjects and you have probably already learnt how to extract information from charts. Your task in design and communication is to know how to translate raw numbers into intelligible statistics which can be easily understood.

Translating numbers into charts and graphs, and having the ability to know which is the most appropriate type to use, is often the task of the graphic designer. A company might employ a graphic designer to produce its annual report. The report will contain all the facts relating to the company, such as production figures, profits and assets. It is the designer's job to present the facts so that they will

make sense to the shareholders. The report has to be designed carefully if it is to be effective.

Charts and diagrams are valuable tools for presenting research data collected at the outset of a project. For example, **anthropometric** statistics (about the human body) would need to be gathered when investigating the size and spacing of seating to design, for example, the layout of a restaurant. This information could be most easily analysed if it were firstly displayed visually in the form or charts or graphs. In this form **modes**, **means** and **statistical deviations** are more easily understood.

However, statistics can produce false conclusions. A frequently quoted, rather cynical comment is 'There are lies, damned lies and statistics'. The art of the statistician is about trying to reveal the truth, but the way in which the information is displayed also requires skill and imagination. Most of us find raw figures rather difficult to digest. Diagrams reveal the pattern and shape of a complex situation. A map provides a bird's eye view of a town or a country, similarly a diagram gives meaning to a numerically complex situation at a single glance.

Types of charts

There are four different types of charts which we need to look at in detail:
- **Line chart**.
- **Bar chart** or **histogram**.
- **Pie chart**.
- **Pictorial chart** or **ideograph**.

General principles

1 Keep charts simple, produce a different chart for each set of statistics, do not crowd information.
2 Edit out all superfluous information such as unnecessary lines, numbers and words. Avoid the use of keys if possible, and round off numbers.
3 Keep titles short, use capital letters and if possible, keep legends horizontal.
4 Aim to present a true picture of the facts, avoid patterns which might cause an optical illusion or visual ambiguity.
5 Select suitable scales for the horizontal and vertical axes which will not distort the statistics.

The line chart

This is the simplest of charts. A number of points are plotted and then joined by a straight line. Several values can be plotted in a small space, allowing visual comparisons to be made quickly. The plotted line will describe clearly any changes which have taken place for any period of time, e.g. weekly, monthly or yearly.

Line charts illustrate many factors such as fluctuations and comparisons, which can be easily read.

The bar chart

Easy to understand and simple to produce, this chart is used to describe simple fixed values in a certain time period. A bar chart should always start from zero and the bars should be the same width. Make sure the bars are not too close together unless you are producing a solid chart (this type can be difficult to read). Other forms of bar charts are the compound and the multi-bar. Bar charts have their limitations — they do not allow for comparisons to be easily made between a number of bar charts, and they are not easily read. Line charts might not be as visually compelling but they often produce a better solution. Bar charts are designed to hit the eye with information about a single factor.

The pie chart

A pie chart is a circle which has been cut into segments. Each segment is a percentage of the total converted into radian measurement. For example, 10 per cent of the total would be represented by a 36 degree segment. It is normal practice for the segments to run from the largest to the smallest in a clockwise direction. It can be more difficult to compare the areas of segments than the lengths of bars. When comparing two pie charts it is difficult to calculate accurately from charts which have the correct visual impact. In the example shown the second chart is meant to show a 100 per cent increase on the first. If the diameter is increased by the correct amount the area is quadrupled, if the area is doubled the result is a slightly larger circle and the visual impact is lost.

Pie charts have a good visual effect but they can only be used to show the break-down of a total — how the cake is divided up!

The pictorial chart

This is visually the most striking form of chart. It is useful when making a presentation or in an exhibition. The most common form is when a series of graphic symbols are used to replace the bars on a chart. This is known as a **pictogram**. The symbol is used to attract attention but this is done at the expense of accuracy. This can be overcome by adding a few additional facts. Keep the symbols simple and always the same size. Pie charts can also be adapted and made more pictorial. This is frequently done by changing the shape of the pie. This treatment can also be applied to produce statistical maps or cartograms. When wishing to draw a number of identical pictures make use of either a light box or photocopier.

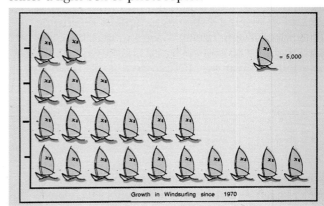

Growth in Windsurfing since 1970

Activity 81

Travelling can often be a hazardous experience. Whichever form of travel we select, e.g. trains, cars or planes, there is the chance that we might be involved in an accident. Your task is to represent the following statistics graphically. The information gives the risk of death per million passengers for every 100 miles travelled by a variety of transport types.

car driver	0.93	heavy goods driver	0.37
pedal cyclist	11.5	train passenger	0.03
bus passenger	0.09	motor cyclist	22.2
airline passenger	0.10		

Select two ways of illustrating these statistics and produce, in both cases, a visually striking presentation.

The illustrations on this page show how the graphic designer can use charts creatively. Look at these examples and identify the types of charts which have been used. The designer has presented the facts imaginatively and a high standard of communication has been achieved.

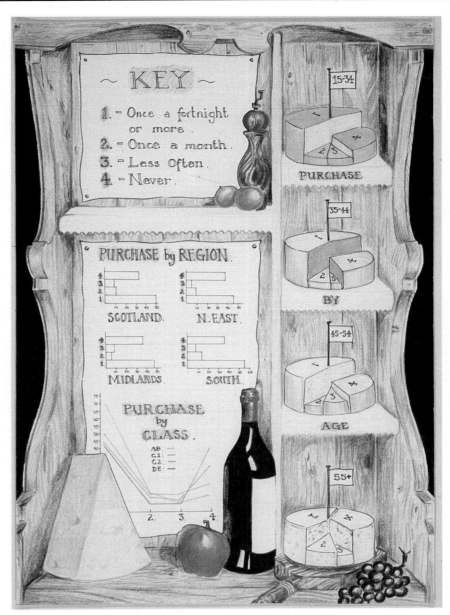

Activity 82

The habit of drinking bottled water is growing rapidly. In 1987 the total UK market was worth £100 million. The cost of a bottle is the sum of a number of factors. Produce a diagram to illustrate the following statistics:

5%	**manufacturer's profit**
15%	**Value Added Tax**
15%	**advertising**
25%	**cost of bottle, label etc.**
8%	**processing water**
12%	**transport costs**
20%	**retail mark-up**

Activity 83

Devise a questionnaire related to a particular pursuit, for example, television viewing habits, types of food eaten, newspapers and magazines which are read. Make the questionnaire reasonably simple and easy to answer, limit it to a maximum of ten questions. Conduct a survey using your questionnaire with a minimum sample of 25 people. Process the information you collect and then present it as an A4 information sheet using appropriate graphical means to illustrate your results.

If the facilities are available attempt one of the above activities using an appropriate piece of computer software.

Manipulating the figures

The most commonly used method of distorting the figures is to select an inappropriate scale for either the vertical or horizontal axis or both. Look at the six examples of a line graph. Each is based on the same set of statistics, yet the visual impression created by each chart is quite different. An increase in sales can be made to look quite impressive by either compressing the horizontal scale or expanding the vertical scale. Another trick is to use an incomplete vertical scale (the scale does not start at zero). This will also produce exaggerations; differences appear greater and trends more dramatic.

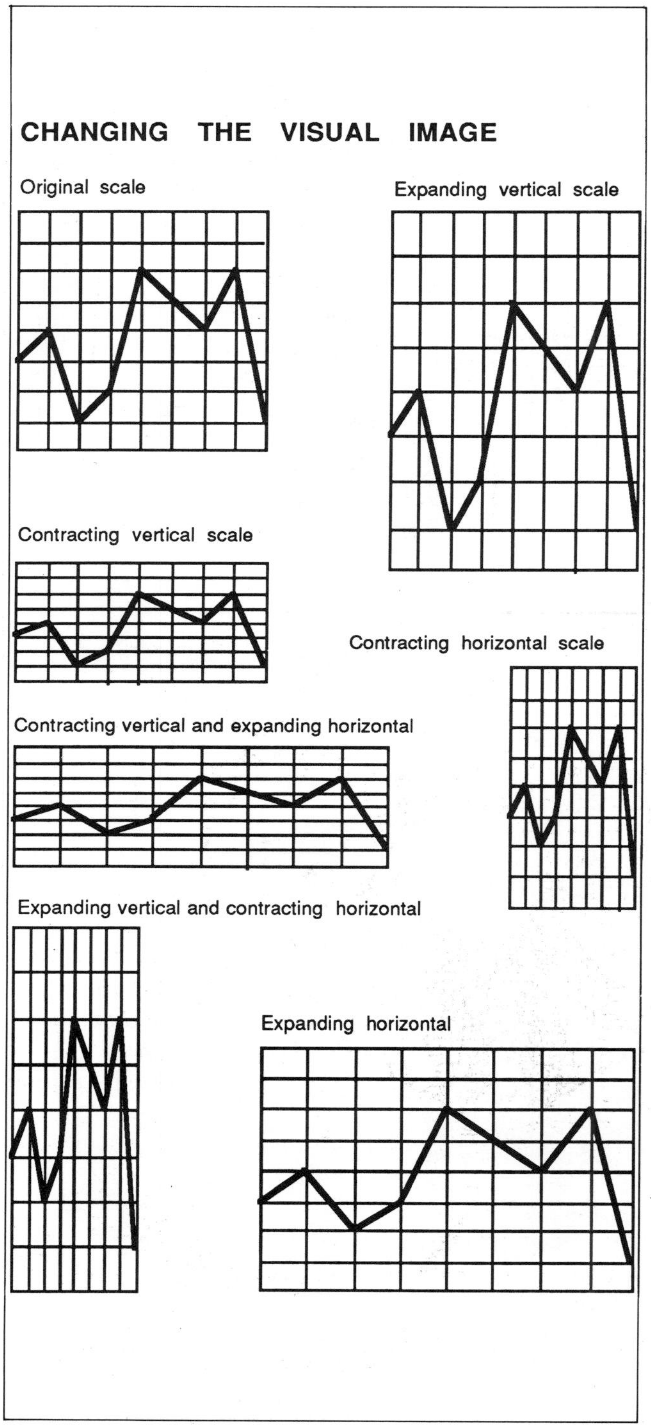

CHANGING THE VISUAL IMAGE

Original scale

Expanding vertical scale

Contracting vertical scale

Contracting horizontal scale

Contracting vertical and expanding horizontal

Expanding vertical and contracting horizontal

Expanding horizontal

Activity 84* — Research

Visit your local shopping centre and carry out the following tasks:

1 *Make a list of all the different retail outlets in the shopping centre. Classify them in two ways, first by type of product or service, e.g. shoe shops or travel agents; second whether the shop has branches nationally, regionally or just locally. For example the Body Shop is national (in fact international), Anglian Bakers is regional, and Truro Wine Stores is local. Present the information gathered in a graphically interesting way.*

2 *Select one of the shops which is part of a national chain. Conduct a survey of its corporate identity. Collect examples of its visual identity. Do this using drawings, taking photographs and by collecting examples. Carry out some market research to discover what image and reputation the company has. Survey about twenty people.*

   Start by establishing a short questionnaire. Try to limit it to half a dozen questions to which simple answers can be given. Here is an example of a poor question, and underneath the question asked more precisely. This enables the information to be collated and conclusions arrived at. If you have the facilities, produce your questionnaire using wordprocessing facilities on a microcomputer. Present your survey in the form of a memorandum from a consultant to the shop manager.

Activity 85* — Design project

Design a corporate image for your local take-away. When embarking on this project it is best to select a local shop rather than a national fast-food company such as Macdonalds. If you do not have a suitable take-away decide on a type of food and think of an appropriate name. The range of possibilities will include fish and chips, Indian, American (hamburgers, shakes etc.), Chinese, Italian (pizza), baked potato, and any others you can think of or believe have potential.

The first stage will be to design an appropriate logo or trademark. When doing this remember that a local shop may have financial constraints. This might mean that only one single colour can be used.

Once the logo is finalized, design and make a carrier bag from a suitable material such as brown paper or polythene. Then transfer your logo to the bag. The most straightforward way of doing this will be with a paper mask and a Letrajet. Complete the project by adding the logo to any other items which might be required such as serviettes, food containers and expanded polystyrene cups for hot sauces. If you feel the product is best packed in a box, which might be the case for a pizzeria, then design the box and add the logo to it.

Make a display of your completed scheme. If you have based your project on an actual shop, show it to the proprietor — he or she may like your design!

Activity 86*

Many of the large DIY and garden centres are owned by famous high street retailers, for example Homebase by Sainsburys, Do-It-All by WH Smith and B & Q by Woolworths. Another high street retailer has decided to launch a number of out-of-town centres aimed at the house owner. The first task is to come up with a suitable name for the chain of centres and an appropriate logo. The second phase of the project is to determine the main areas within the store such as plumbing, lighting, kitchens, gardens etc. A symbol is required for each area so that customers can quickly locate where the goods are which they require. Ensure that the symbols you design and the logo share a visual identity, if only in colour.

Activity 87

Produce a flow diagram which will illustrate the actions to be carried out when planning and taking a holiday. Your diagram should start at the point of obtaining information about possible destinations and should end with arrival at your chosen resort. The more exotic the destination the more complex the diagram will be. Start by producing a diagram for a holiday in the UK, then add the extra actions for a European holiday by car using a cross-channel ferry, and finally look at a holiday to a South American destination by aircraft.

For each diagram mark the critical path and state the number of activities in each case.

MODEL MAKING

Two-dimensional card models

Card is a readily available material which is reasonably cheap. Often scrap card can be used for model making if you just need to explore an idea. For other projects it is worth using good quality card. An idea can be presented very well using card to give a solid feel to a two-dimensional view.

A wide range of cutters is available for cutting card. A scalpel or craft knife is obviously essential. A good quality cutting board will also make the task easier and help produce better results. Circle cutters, contour cutters and ones which produce perforations are also useful.

Several sheets of orthographic sketches have been produced and a number of these ideas have been translated into simple card models. A glossy card has been used for the handle and a metallized card for the blade to make it realistic. The designer can now select the most suitable solution and develop the finished design. Card has been used to clarify the idea. Card is being used as an alternative to drawing. It produces a more precise image and also forces the designer to start thinking about the solid form of the object.

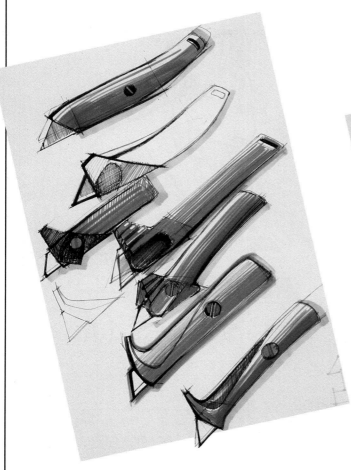

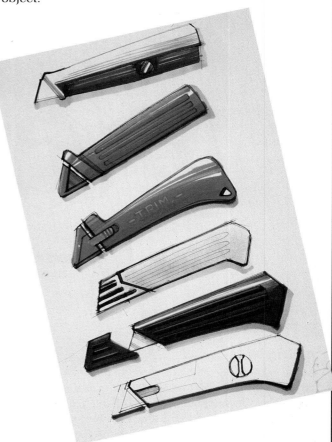

Example

Craft knives come in a variety of forms: Stanley knives, snap-off blades, retractable blades etc. In school you may even find yourself using a home-made version, for example a piece of sharpened hacksaw blade in a wooden handle. Many cutting knives are based on Stanley knife blades, and this is the designer's brief in this example. The handle of the knife is to be injection moulded and either a safety cap or a retraction system is required.

Activity 88

Make card models of the operational ends of two common domestic gadgets — a tin opener and a potato peeler. Both require moulded plastic handles. Follow through the process described in relation to the craft knife and produce a range of possible designs modelled in card.

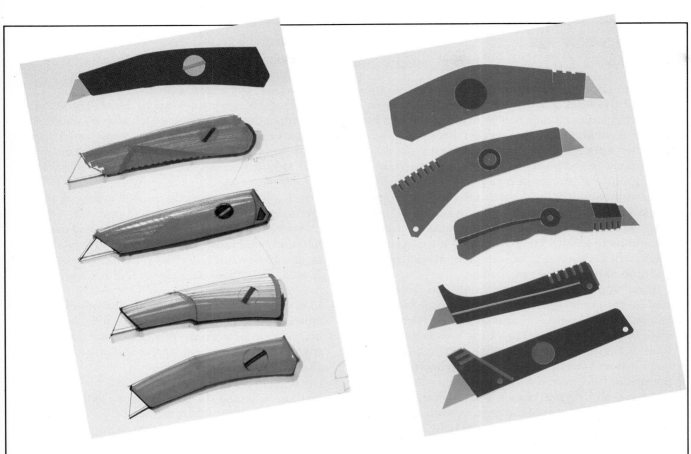

Activity 89

An adjustable wrench, as shown, is made from two drop forgings and a machined pivot pin. The operational end of the tool works very well but the handles leave a lot to be desired. Ergonomically they are not very satisfactory. Moulded plastic handles slid over the metal ones would appear to be a good idea. Using sketches and then articulating card models produce some possible solutions to this problem.

Activity 90

A range of sealers and glues can be purchased which fit a standard gun for dispensing. The handles of this gun are uncomfortable to hold and do not provide sufficient force for many people. Redesign the operational elements of the tool and produce an articulated card model of your best solution.

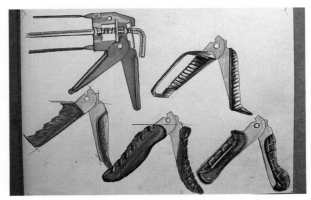

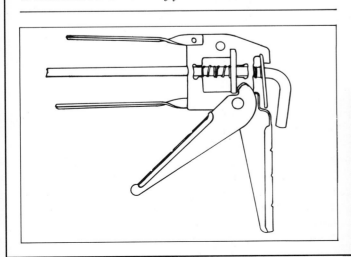

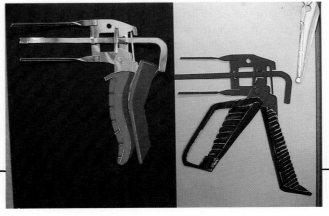

Moving models

The term **paper** or **cardboard engineering** is often used for this kind of activity. You have already seen how articulating models can be made in the section on technical graphics. This section deals with pop-ups and sectional models. In recent years pop-up cards and books have once again become very popular. If you are given a pop-up card examine it carefully. Some of these cards are very ingenious. Books including pop-ups attempt to make a subject come to life by presenting the information three-dimensionally. Frequently they are used in books which describe how something works, such as the human body, a car or a camera.

The first pop-up books were published around the middle of the nineteenth century and they told the stories of nursery rhymes and fairy tales. Primarily, as now, they were designed to amuse. About the same time sectional illustrations were being included in technical and scientific books to describe visually to the reader the internal workings or structure of a mechanism or natural object. The illustrations on this page show a turn of the century sectional diagram of a car and a 1980 pop-up book of the car. The car itself has obviously changed a great deal, and so has the complexity of information and the way it is presented.

Key points

- Remember what was said on the previous page regarding knives and cutting boards.
- When planning a card, take great care with marking out. Use a solid line to denote a line to be cut and a dotted line one which is to be folded. It is also worth using a different type of dotted line to indicate an up or hill fold from a down or valley fold. Decide yourself: a different colour is probably the simplest.
- Before folding scour along the line to ensure the crease is accurate and crisp. Scouring will compress the fibres in the paper. This will make it fold and bend more easily. You can buy special scouring tools but a dry ball-point pen does just as well. If you have difficulty in folding, use a steel rule to fold against.
- Glue with great care — do not use too much. Use either a white PVA adhesive in stick form, as this makes it easier to apply, or a petroleum based glue such as UHU. A cocktail stick is useful for applying glue and spreading it evenly.
- Use flaps to join paper edge to edge. A very neat method is to pass the flap through a slot and then glue it to the back. This can only be used on internal joints. Do not cut through the front or back of a card.

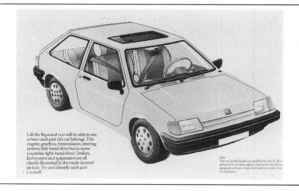

Lift the flaps and you will be able to see where each part of a car belongs. The engine, gearbox, transmission, steering system (left-hand drive but in some countries right-hand drive), brakes, fuel system and suspension are all clearly illustrated in the multi-layered picture. Try and identify each part yourself.

Pop-up books and cards

There are quite a number of simple mechanisms which can be employed in cards and books. A book called *Paper Engineering* by Mark Hiner describes how to make ten. If you wish to become more proficient in making these devices refer to his book. We are going to examine four basic mechanisms.

Mechanism 1 — V forms

This is a simple yet very useful mechanism. The opening of the card causes the V form to stand up and project from the card. The mechanism will be symmetrical either side of the centre line. The V form can be adapted in a number of ways:

1 The V form A will stand vertical because the angle between the fold lines is a right angle. The one marked B will stand at an angle because the angle between the fold lines is less than 90 degrees. What will happen if the angle between the fold lines is obtuse?

2 The V form is strong enough to pull up both vertical and horizontal additional layers. More than one V form can be included in a card.

3 The centre of a V form can be cut away to produce an arch effect.

Check the position of your V form before gluing it down. You must make sure it is hidden within the card when it is laid flat.

Mechanism 2 — Parallel layers

This is a very useful mechanism which allows a series of parallel layers to be created giving an impression of depth. Drawings can be cut up and reassembled on different layers. The edges of the various layers must always be parallel to each other and to one of the sides of the card. As with the V form the layers can be used to pull up other layers.

Take care that the card is large enough to house the layers. Usually these cards are designed to be viewed when the corner between the back and front of the card is 90 degrees.

Mechanism 3 – Moving arms

This mechanism is a development of the V form device and it operates using two sides of a square-based pyramid. It can either be made by cutting the card or by including the V form in a parallel layer. Once you have grasped the principle you will realize that the extended arm is just amplifying the movement. The arm can extend in any direction and there could be more than two arms operated from the device.

Mechanism 4 – Self erecting box

This mechanism involves a box which collapses flat when the card is closed and erects to form a solid shape when the card is opened. It is basically a collapsing M shape with added ends. Again master the idea and then adapt it. The box does not have to be square but it does have to be square about the centre line. The top does not have to be flat. If, for example, it is a house, it can have a sloping roof, but do not connect the roof to the central support.

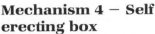

Activity 91

Design and make a pop-up card for one of the following occasions:
Valentine's Day, Hallowe'en, or a congratulations card for passing design and communication at GCSE

Activity 92

Design and make a pop-up page for a book based on one of the following subjects:
volcanoes, bicycles, Art Deco, a famous building, an historical event or an animal

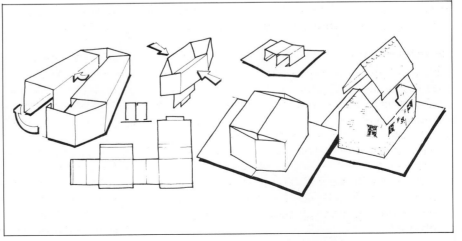

Block and foam modelling

When designing a product there comes a point when the designer must start to work in three dimensions. It is very difficult to judge from a drawing the exact proportions of an object and the relationship of the various elements. It is also much easier for someone without a designer's eye to appreciate what the end product will look like from a model. A range of materials is used depending on the requirements of the model. A car is modelled in a special wax known as **clavant**. This material can be shaped with great accuracy and can be built up and carved away at will. Product designers frequently use **foamed** or **aerated polymers**. The most common are **styrofoam**, **high density polystyrene foam** and **polyurethane foam**. More detailed block models are made out of wood such as **jelutong**, which is easy to work as it has virtually no grain. The objective in modelling in these materials is not to produce an exact working replica of the production model but to produce a solid or block form of the object. The doors will not open on the car, and the push buttons will not operate on a foam phone.

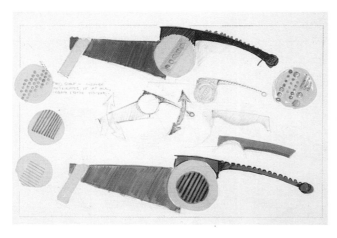

Example 1

Foam is excellent for exploring possible forms, in this case the possible appearance of a small portable dustbag, the type of vacuum cleaner you use when cleaning a car. Sketches are used to sort out the possible arrangement of the elements — handle, motor, collecting container and nozzle. Often the elements in a product are packaged in a moulded shell which disguises them. In this case the designer wanted the elements to have an independent visual integrity. The geometric forms which result give the product visual character, similar to a Memphis style. Sketches develop into more detailed orthographic views and crude pictorials drawn directly with markers. The designer is now ready to produce some solid models.

Foam can be cut very easily. Professional model makers use wire cutters which are electrically heated but this is dangerous in a school situation — you should only cut the foam using mechanical methods. A band saw can be used to cut basic shapes or alternatively hand saws such as coping or hacksaws can be used. Surforms and files can be used to create curves and detailing which can be finished to a good surface using abrasive paper.

A number of simple geometric shapes which represent the various elements of the dustbug have been produced in foam, assembled and then painted with white emulsion to give them unity. In this way a number of possibilities are quickly produced for evaluation. The designer can now select the best concept and set about developing the idea into a complete design.

Foam can be joined in a number of ways. A wide range of glues can be used such as PVA woodwork glue. Be careful though, a number of solvent and impact adhesives will dissolve the foam very rapidly, always check it out first on a piece of scrap foam. Double-sided tape can also be used if the surfaces to be joined are making good contact. Dowels are often a good idea to help hold pieces together; wooden cocktail sticks are excellent as they are easy to push into the foam.

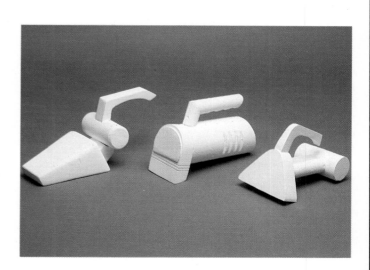

Example 2

Foam can also be used to produce more finished models providing the degree of detailing required is not too great. In this example the designer was interested in converting a lever staple gun into one with a trigger action. Both the visual appearance and internal mechanism of the existing solutions were examined. The new principle was explored to check its feasibility. A simple orthographic rendering was produced and on the basis of this a foam model was made.

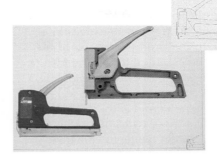

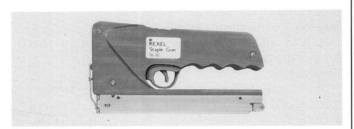

The main body was shaped carefully in foam and then details were added using other materials. For example, the cartridge which holds the staples is made out of sheet polystyrene, the trigger is carved out of a soft wood such as balsa or jelutong, in fact any material can be used if it does the job! Once shaped the parts can be painted. Emulsion paint is the most suitable for foam although it does produce a matt finish. If a gloss surface is required the surface must first be sealed. Emulsion paint with added plaster of paris is ideal. This can be a very time-consuming process as the filler will need to be rubbed down and the finished model is pretty delicate. If you require a model of real detail with a highly reflective finish it would be more sensible to use jelutong. An excellent finish can be obtained using an airbrush and acrylic paints – prime the surface with emulsion prior to spraying.

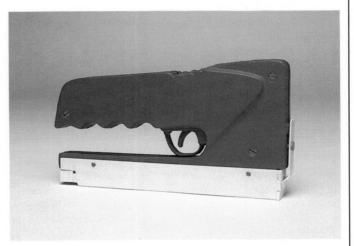

As you can see, the finished model is quite compelling in its realism. However it does not work. The secret is given away as soon as the object is picked up, as it is so much lighter than the real thing.

Tips

When shaping foam start by cutting out in paper the front elevation of the object. Glue this paper cut-out to the foam block and use it as a template. If you can use the same principle for the end elevation as well, it will make your task easier. It is a good idea to reassemble the parts including the waste before you try to cut the end profile.

Detail can be added by dissolving the surface in a process similar to etching. The best solvent is the fluid sold for bleeding one spirit-based marker into another. It can be bought either in a bottle or as a marker pen. It is more controllable in the marker pen form. The marker pen can be used to add details such as break lines – the joint line between two mouldings. All you need to do is draw accurately on the surface – the pen will do the rest. For deeper impressions use the pen over and over again. Experiment to discover the degree of undercutting which takes place. For more detailed work use a mask as in the example shown.

Other uses of foam

An architect may use foam in a similar way to a product designer except that, as in all architectural modelling, it will be scaled down rather than 1:1. The overall form of a building might quickly be given substance using foam, and possibilities explored. It is also used to create townscapes. An architect may have surrounding buildings modelled in foam whilst the building to be designed is modelled in more detail. Urban planners may also use the material to model town centres as it is quick and easy to work with.

Expanded foam is used a great deal in the theatre and television to create scenery and replicas of real objects. Window dressers use it for similar reasons. In such situations the foam must be treated with a fire retardant as it is highly inflammable.

Activity 93

Select a consumer product such as a telephone, iron, camera or hairdryer. Analyse what is currently available to the consumer and then attempt to produce a different possible solution aimed at a specific market. Model your solution in foam. Tip – a good starting point for an analysis is a mail-order catalogue.

Prototype models

Foam, paper and card are all useful materials for making models when designing. Eventually a designer will need to confirm his or her ideas in a more detailed model. In the professional world of design this model will be essential to sell the idea to the client. Often the client will not be a designer so he or she may not appreciate a design from a drawing, and the prototype model is therefore essential. Designers make these types of models for different reasons. An architect needs to convince not only the client that the building is the one wanted but also the planning authorities and those responsible for the environment. A product designer needs to sell the idea to the client who will then have to invest a great deal of money in setting up production.

A car manufacturer will produce as many as 50 prototypes. Although hand built, they will represent exactly the production model. These models will be used for tests and performance trials. A graphic designer will produce a finished piece of artwork for approval. If accepted the packaging or poster will be reproduced photographically from the artwork. Generally we do not describe pieces of graphics as models, but in reality they are as they are exact representations of the finished article.

What kind of prototype models are appropriate to this subject? The answer is whatever model is required as part of your course work or major project. Perhaps the three areas which you are most likely to be involved in are product modelling, architectural models and packaging prototypes. We shall examine these three areas in detail.

Packaging

The most common materials used in packaging are card and thermoplastics, of which PVC and low density polythene are the most important. Unit 4 — Technical graphics has already examined aspects of packaging in relation to card and a simple

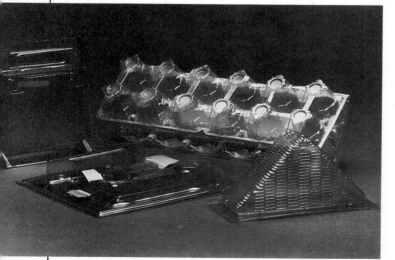

explanation of vacuum forming is also given. In this section we shall look more closely at vacuum forming and PVC.

The photograph shows a range of PVC packs. There are three types: blister packs which are always mounted on backing cards; vacuum formed containers with a hinge which fold into a complete container, such as an egg box; and containers which are developments, folded up and then glued. The egg box container type is extremely complex and requires a very accurate mould. It is probably too difficult to make in school although it is possible to make a box with a lid. Blister packs and folded boxes can be made in school.

Vacuum forming
Making the mould

- **Material** — Before looking at each of the packaging types in turn, we need to know some general points about vacuum forming. The first step is to make the mould. In school the most suitable material is jelutong. When using thin PVC great care has to be taken to create smooth surfaces. A poor surface finish on the mould will result in a distorted surface and a lack of clarity in the moulded pack. Commerically metal moulds are used with a highly polished surface, but these are extremely time-consuming to make. Do not wax or paint the surface of the mould as this can cause problems when a hot plastic sheet comes into contact with the mould.

- **Mould design** — The simplest type of mould is a **plug mould**, a replica of the shape you wish to form, modified so that the finished moulding can be removed from the mould. The mould must have a draft angle on all sloping sides of at least 2 degrees. As PVC is thin you can sometimes get away with a reduced draft angle. It depends on the shape and size of the mould. Try to avoid sharp corners and corners where the included angle is less than 90 degrees, as this will cause webbing. The mould must be vented to prevent air being trapped in enclosed hollows and cavities. This can be done by drilling fine holes with sharpened piano wire. When making a mould, imagine you are making a jelly — the moulding must come off as easily as a jelly comes out of a mould.

- **Mounting the mould** — Often you require a flat surface of material around the mould. This is especially the case with blister packs. This means mounting the mould on a piece of flat board, such as hardboard, and drilling a series of holes around the mould. Alternatively place the mould on a piece of thickish card and using a pin, prick the card around the edge of the mould. It is a good idea to use a small piece of double-sided tape to locate the mould and prevent it from moving. It is possible to buy card which allows air to pass through it, which makes the process much simpler.

VACUUM FORMING

WARM A TUMBLER IN HOT WATER.... PLACE KITCHEN CLING FILM TIGHTLY OVER THE NECK AND ALLOW TO COOL....

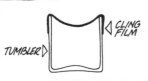

TUMBLER ▷ ◁ CLING FILM

THE FILM WILL BE SUCKED INTO THE TUMBLER AS THE AIR INSIDE COOLS AND A **VACUUM** FORMS.

WE USE THIS PRINCIPLE IN **VACUUM FORMING**... FIRST THE PLASTIC IS HEATED TO MAKE IT SOFT...

SEAL   SEAL

....THEN THE AIR IS SUCKED OUT.

WHEN THE PLASTIC HAS COOLED AND BECOME HARD AGAIN IT CAN BE REMOVED.

THIS PROCESS IS USED MOSTLY FOR PACKAGING SUCH AS MEAT, JAM, YOGURT, CAKES, ETC.

THE REVERSE OF THIS PROCESS IS CALLED **BLOW MOULDING** AND IS USED TO FORM PLASTIC BOTTLES AND JARS.

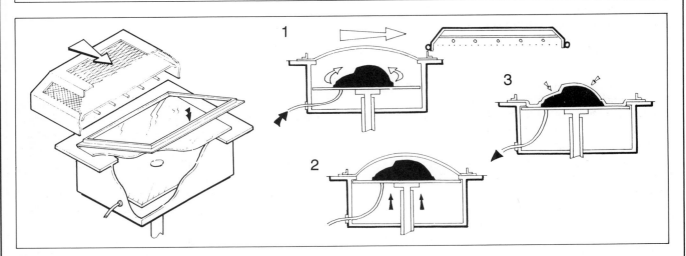

- **Moulding** — When your mould is ready you can carry out the forming process. Exactly how this process takes place will depend on the type of vacuum forming machine you have. The principle of most machines is the same.
1. The mould is positioned centrally in the frame. The table is lowered and the thermoplastic sheet clamped in place.
2. The sheet is heated until it becomes plastic. PVC firstly distorts, then becomes flat again. It has reached the correct temperature when a small impression quickly disappears. Do not overheat, if you do the PVC will start to give off fumes. The PVC will also be so soft that it will form so tightly around the mould it will be difficult to remove the moulding.
3. When the plastic is at the correct temperature the mould is raised into the sheet and a vacuum is created between the plastic and the mould, causing the plastic to collapse onto the mould.
4. Once the plastic has chilled slightly the air flow is reversed, the vacuum broken and the mould drops out leaving the moulding.
5. The excess material can be carefully cut away leaving a finished moulding.

Blister pack

This is the very simplest type of moulding. A plug is made which resembles the shape to be packaged. Remember the shape should be simplified as much as possible whilst ensuring that the object will be held securely. Once the mould has been made it has to be secured to the backing board. If it is to be secured permanently a clear adhesive should be used. However, as you are making a prototype you may wish to get to the product inside, so hinge the blister pack using double-sided tape. Another option is to fold the blister around the board as shown and locate it using tabs.

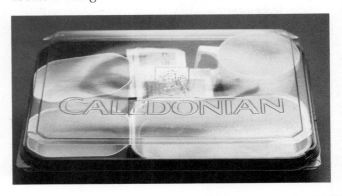

Folded pack

This type of package is obviously very similar to working in card. The first stage is to work out the development. This is then transferred to the PVC. The best method of marking the material is to use a pin, but do not press too hard. A fine scratch line will also help when you come to fold up the pack. A dry biro is also useful to help focus a bend and produce a sharp corner. This material will also curve uniformly so cylindrical shapes can be created. It can be used in conjunction with card to create windows and clear shells fitting into card bases.

PVC vacuum formed box

The best way of describing this process is to use an example. The brief set was to design, make and then pack a biscuit which will appeal to a specified market sector. The final pack should contain a dozen biscuits.

This brief obviously requires a great deal of design work, but we shall focus on the relevent aspects. Once the biscuit shape had been designed a cutter was made. This was also vacuum formed. The next step was to make the packaging. A mould was made with wells to accommodate the biscuits and protect them. The mould was not given a base as the perforated metal on the table of the vacuum former produces a texture in the plastic which stiffens it; this is also done commercially. Once a forming of the mould has been taken a thin top is fixed to the mould. This now forms the mould for the lid. Thin detail can be added to the top of the lid, such as the name of the biscuit and the company's trademark, for example. This detail can be made out of cardboard or thin polystyrene sheet. Either wil result in a good precise moulding. Follow the stages through in the photographs.

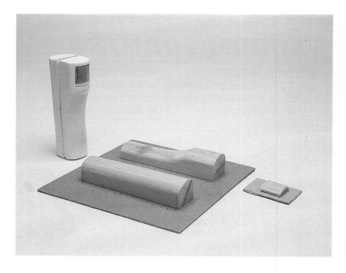

The photograph above shows the moulds used to vacuum form the casing of a prototype model of a torch.

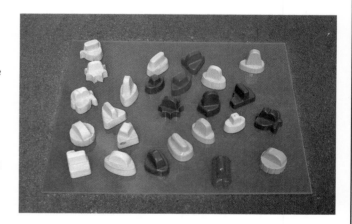

*Activity 94**

Have a go at the biscuit design project described above. You could produce the biscuits to a known recipe or you could have a go at designing your own. The following questions are ones you will need to answer.

- *Has the product got a clear identity?*
- *Does the identity relate well to the selected market sector?*
- *What qualities should the biscuit have — shape, texture, colour, taste, etc.?*
- *Should the shape of the biscuit be one that packs economically? One that relates to the pack shape? Just one or a range of shapes?*
- *How should the pack be made and how will the necessary information be incorporated.*

Product models

As in any model making, anything goes providing you achieve the effect you are seeking. Product modelling is the art of illusion. It is the skill of making something appear as something it is not, or as if it has been made in a way that it has not. Product modelling is nearly always done at a scale of 1:1 (full size). The industrial or product designer is often concerned with objects which will eventually be injection moulded. As we have already noted, making moulds for injection moulding is an expensive business, so realistic models, true in every detail to the eventual product, are needed. This is a highly skilful task and involves a number of techniques and a lot of patience. It is something you can do using some tricks and processes appropriate to the school situation.

Materials

The basic material to be used in school is sheet polystyrene. It is cheap and straightforward to work. It can be shaped quickly by scoring the surface with a sharp knife and then cracking along the score line. It can be sawn easily with piercing or coping saws and files. Because it is quick to shape, it is obviously very soft which means it marks easily. This means protecting the material as much as you can. Do not, for example, hold the material in a vice with knurled jaws.

Polystyrene sheet comes in a wide range of thicknesses which are vital to detailed model making. It can also be vacuum formed accurately. It is quick and easy to join pieces together using solvents and cements. Polystyrene cement, which comes in a tube, is good for initial box building. The solvents, which are liquid and come in a bottle or can, are quicker to use and essential for detailed work. Quite often a basic shape is produced by vacuum forming and then additional pieces are added.

Polystyrene does have drawbacks. It is difficult to spray as cellulose sprays do not adhere well to the surface (the exception being matt black). Once sprayed it is best left alone. Do not attempt to rub the surface down with wet and dry paper. If you do, you will find that the paint will peel off.

A material which has all the advantages of polystyrene and does spray well is ABS (acrylontrile butadiene styrene). It is used by professional model makers but unfortunately it is much more expensive than polystyrene. It is worth using for small scale model making, where cost is not so important. Acrylic can also be used but unfortunately it does not come in thin sheets. Acrylic tends to be carved away to form the required shape rather than fabricated as with polystyrene. Occasionally aluminium might also be used, but a different range of techniques must be employed.

Observation

Before you attempt to model a possible product you should first examine some injection moulded products to see what features are common to articles produced by this process.

- **Break lines** — Most products are made up of more than one moulding. Butt joints are far less common than a recessed shoulder which results in the distinctive break line. The reason for this is that mouldings often distort very slightly on cooling. Distortion would result in butt joints appearing irregular. Consequently designers make a virtue of necessity and make a feature of the joint line between mouldings.

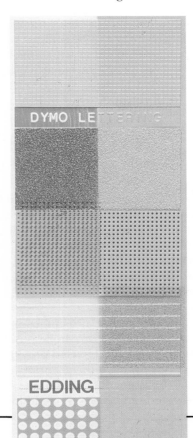

- **Surface pattern** – Moulds for injection moulding dies are produced on spark erosion and milling machines. Such machines produce geometrically precise patterns with ease, especially now that they are computer controlled. The resulting upstanding patterns are a common feature on mouldings. Frequently they provide grip but they are also used to provide a visual feature. In most instances these patterns are upstanding as this is the cheapest production method. It is a positive process in the mould-making procedure. This means that the required pattern is milled into the surface of the mould as a depression.
- **Surface texture** – Many injection mouldings are smooth and glossy but others have a granular texture. These textures, which vary in roughness, are, like a pattern, used either to provide grip or alternatively to create a visual feature.
- **Lettering** – Raised lettering is a very common feature. The company's name, the country or origin and instructions are often proud of the surface. Like a pattern on the surface, this is the cheapest way of including information as an integral part of the moulding.

   Alternatively, lettering might be screen printed on to a product. Dry transfer lettering such as Letraset or Eddings can be used to simulate these effects. On a hard surface the rub-down lettering is quite hard wearing.

All of these features will make your models appear realistic. The next step is to see how they can be recreated.

Break lines

The simplest way of including these is by fabrication. Build up a series of layers to create the required effect. Alternatively they can be scraped out using a specially ground tool in either a marking gauge or a scribing block. This technique is particularly useful on curved surfaces.

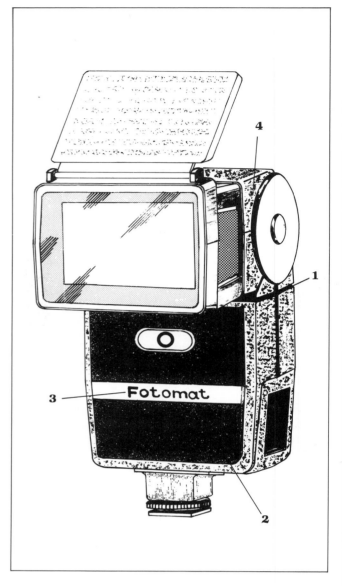

1 Break line
2 Surface texture
3 Lettering
4 Surface pattern

Surface pattern

The cheapest way of simulating patterns is die cut self-adhesive paper labels. They are available in a wide range of shapes and sizes, dots, squares, strips etc. It is vital that the paper textures are transferred to your model without disturbing the mechanical regularity. This can be done by lifting the shapes from the non-stick surface using low tack masking film and then placing them precisely in the correct position on the model.

   Vacuum formed sheeting and embossed plastic sheet can also be used. These can be purchased or home made. Anything can be used provided it can be mounted securely on the surface and it can be spray finished. Spraying is the final operation which links all the various elements into a unified model.

Surface texture

On flat surfaces the easiest way to create a textured surface is to use coarse wet and dry paper. The best way to apply it to the surface is to use spraymount. It is a good idea to always place the wet and dry paper in a recess so that the edge is well disguised. On curved surfaces it is much trickier, but some success can be achieved in the following way. Spray the completed model with spray mount and then dust it or roll it in an even grit such as the one used in a sand blaster. The difficulty is in obtaining an even surface. This can be improved if the grit is placed in a fluidizing tank and the model with its sprayed surface is swirled around in the tank. The grit will only adhere to the surfaces which are sticky so masking is carried out at the spraying stage.

Lettering

There are a number of ways in which relief lettering can be added to a model.

1 Slater's Plastikard lettering consists of a sheet of injection moulded letters which can be mounted on a model. It is important that the letters are mounted precisely and accurately — always work to a pencil line, it will disappear under the spray. The best device for picking the letters up is a needle pushed into a cork. Apply solvent sparingly. Do not flood the surface as the sharp detail of the letter will be lost. This type of lettering comes in four sizes — 1.5, 3.0, 5.0 and 8.0 mm. The smallest size is extremely difficult to use.

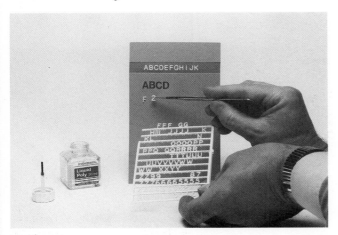

2 Die cut lettering is available in two forms. Plastic die cut lettering, such as that produced by Edding, is the most expensive. It is, however, extremely precise and easy to use. It comes with instructions and a simple system to enable accurate usage. Although it does come in three sizes, only the smallest, 7.5 mm high, is suitable for model making. Paper die cut lettering is sold for labelling video tapes. It is much cheaper but less precise.

3 The cheapest and possibly least convincing method is to use dymotape. The tape should be disguised between edges and once sprayed it does achieve a moulded in look.

4 If you require a particular typeface or logo there are two ways in which this can be achieved.

  a Using rub-down transfer lettering, any typeface can be chemically milled or etched out of thin brass shim. Rub the required word on to a piece of brass shim; cover the back surface of the brass with Sellotape and attach a piece of acrylic to the tape (this is to prevent the letters becoming lost in the etch bath). The unwanted brass is then etched away in a ferric chloride bath similar to the type used for printed circuit board work. The brass letters can then be mounted on the model using a solvent cement. This process can be used for producing any small detail or object. It is used a great deal by architectural model makers for producing railings and balustrades, for example.

  b It is possible to photocopy on to thin styrene sheet (depending on the type of photocopier — the feed must be straight, not around rollers). This enables detailed artwork such as a logo to be transferred on to polystyrene. Then it can be cut out precisely and mounted on the model.

Spraying

All of these techniques rely on the final process — spraying — to unite them so that they will appear as a single moulding. When spraying, build up a series of thin coats. Do not overspray as this will result in runs and a ruined model. A priming spray will help adhesion when using cellulose paint. Always spray in a purpose-built spray booth, a well-ventilated room, or outside in a dry, still spot. Make sure the model can be turned easily so all parts of the surface will be covered. With practice, spraying from a distance can produce a texture. If you have used Slater's lettering the paint on the surface can be carefully removed using very fine wet and dry paper to create the effect of a painted raised surface after moulding. This is achieved commercially by passing the moulding under a roller so that all raised up surfaces are coated.

Product modelling – examples

Example 1

This example looks at solid models. The simplest form of an injection moulding consists of a single solid piece of plastic – a windscreen scraper, templates and measures etc. These are the simplest objects to start modelling, as they are not hollow. They do not require a box to be made which is obviously more complex. The brief is to design, make and display a simple 'freebie' which is to be given away with a magazine as a promotional aid.

There is an endless range of possibilities to this brief depending on the magazine you start from. The product has to be reasonably thin, possibly 2 to 3 mm maximum. The example illustrated here is a totally new product which had to be given a name. The magazine is the archaeology issue of the National Trust quarterly journal. The new product is a browel – a combination of a brush and a trowel – used for delicate operations when working on an excavation. The design features a trowel with a brush in the handle. Let us examine the model making stage by stage.

1 The basic blank is cut out of 2 mm-thick polystyrene. An additional piece of 1 mm-thick material is cut to thicken the handle and a window is cut out in which a texture will be mounted.

2 The two pieces are joined together and the edges of the browel are finished off. A piece of coarse wet and dry is cut to provide the texture in the handle. After spraymounting the reverse side it is glued in position. Holes are drilled in the handle to take the brush.

3 The National Trust logo is photocopied on to a thin piece of polystyrene and cut out with great care. It is mounted in the correct position.

4 The freebie is complete and can now be sprayed in a suitable colour. Once sprayed the bristles are fixed into position.

5 A blister pack is made in PVC. The cover of the magazine is adapted with additional graphics to give details of the freebie. The product is mounted under the blister on the cover and the illusion is complete. If manufactured the browel would have to be made in a tough polymer such as glass-filled polycarbonate.

No 46 AUTUMN 1985 50p

National Trust

ARCHAEOLOGY NUMBER

FREE BROWEL

ISSN 0266-8068

Have a go at this brief. Select your own magazine, decide what would be an appropriate freebie, design it and make it. Alternatively it could be a freebie on a food packet such as a breakfast cereal. Another option is to produce a simple product mounted on a backing board which will be purchased in a shop.

Here are some other solutions to this brief.

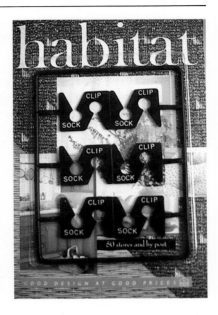

Example 2

The second example deals with packaging a torch. A torch essentially involves three basic units — an energy source, the electrical circuit including a means of controlling it, and the light source including the reflector and lens. The design task is to house these elements in a container which makes using the torch easy and obvious. The container should also be visually suitable and appropriate. This may mean designing with a particular image, purpose or market.

Here are three examples of torch models. They are all working models. The first has been made using vacuum formings. The other two have been fabricated. The design work for these torches is shown on pages 4 and 5.

Let us examine the stages in making one of the fabricated torches, Permabeam.

1 It is in essence three boxes — the stand, the handle and the housing for the switches and light source.

2 The first stage is to make up the slides of the boxes which show the join between the mouldings.

3 The boxes have been fabricated from polystyrene sheet 2 mm thick. The handle and stand are made first of all. The handle fits into the stand and it can be joined together with solvent cement. A fillet (narrow strip) is added with body filler.

4 The housing for the light and switches is built on to the handle. The apertures for the lens and switches are cut in advance. A fillet is also added.

5 The body is carefully rubbed down using the finest wet and dry paper. A radius is added to the corners either by scraping or careful use of wet and dry paper.

6 A very thin sheet of polystyrene is now cut out in the form of the texture to go around the torch. Once finished it is applied with great care using spraymount. Solvent cement can be used on edges if they do not adhere first time.

7 The switches are made and the lettering added. The body is sprayed, the electronics added, lens and switches fixed in position and the torch completed.

Great care and patience must be taken with the finishing stages.

Activity 97*

A charity wishes to produce a money box to encourage people to donate their loose change. They wish to give the money boxes away so that they can be located in homes, offices, classrooms etc. They wish each money box to have a volume of about 500 cm³. For cheapness they will have to be injection moulded. Select a charity of your choice. Design and then make a prototype model of a money box which you think would be suitable.

Architectural models

Types of model

An architect is above all a spatial engineer. Buildings define space, and the best way to understand and solve spatial problems is by making models. But there are many types of models, each made with different objectives in mind:

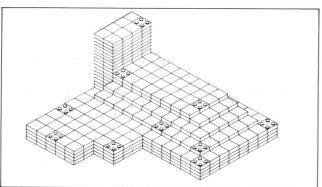

- **Sketch model** — Often first ideas are given a visual form using any objects which come readily to hand: matchboxes, toy bricks, sweetboxes, etc. These can be juggled at will suggesting possible solutions and eliminating others.

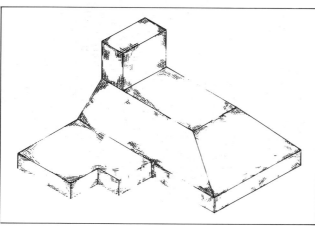

- **Block model** — A refined version of the three-dimensional sketch, this is still an experimental model. Shapes are constructed simply out of paper, card or foam. The design is still fluid, and elements are moved around, recorded in sketches or as photographs. The object is to refine the elements which take up space, no time is wasted at this stage on surface detail.

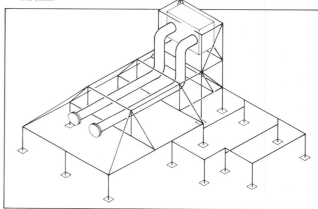

- **Functional model** — This is a sophisticated model to investigate particular aspects of a building such as the structure's strength, provision of essential services, acoustics or lighting.

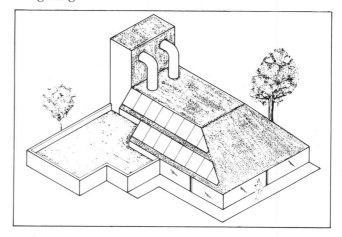

- **Presentation model** – This model represents the architect's complete solution. It is generally produced for promotional purposes and for a non-technical audience. These models are expensive to produce and are only commissioned for important public or commercial buildings.

Scale

The prime difference between an architectural model and a product model is one of scale. The product modeller works at a scale of 1:1 whilst the architectural modeller will make a scale model. The first decision to make, therefore, concerns scale. This will depend on the type of building being modelled. The list below provides a guide to appropriate scales. It is sensible to stick to these scales as architectural model suppliers work to them.

1:20 or 1:50 houses and domestic buildings
1:100 or 1:200 commercial, industrial and public buildings
1:500 or 1:1250 large-scale developments and town models

At the largest scale, 1:20, an average person is 90 mm high, whilst at the smallest, 1:1250, the same person is 1.5 mm tall. The degree of detail required for models obviously varies greatly in relation to the scale.

What type of model to make?

The subject of your model will determine the scale, but before going any further give some careful thought to why are you making a model and what you want it to achieve. If it is your major project you will probably make several types of model as the design progresses. Think about the following points:
- Is it for a specific location?
- Is the model to describe just the exterior? Just the interior? Interior and exterior? Detailed relationship between interior and exterior?
- Is the model to be demountable or is the interior to be viewed through predetermined peepholes?
- What level of detail is required?
- Practical factors – what resources are available? (Time, materials, expertise etc.)

Modelling the landscape

If your model is of a building for a specific location the first step is to model the landscape.

1 Build on a rigid base, something that will provide a sound foundation for your model – blockboard, plywood, chipboard or something similar.
2 Obtain an Ordnance Survey map of the area and photocopy the section you are going to model. Trace out the contours and scale them as appropriate for your model.
3 Contours can then be cut from a sheet material which is of an appropriate thickness. Care must be taken in working out values, otherwise distortions will occur. Cardboard, chipboard, old notice boards or sheet foam are fine if the model is to be smoothed out.

   For example: a model is being made of an estate of houses on a scale of 1:500. The Ordnance Survey map available has a scale of 1:25 000. A 20 mm square on the map when enlarged to the scale of the model will be 1000 mm² (20 x 50 mm). The contour interval on a map of this scale is either 7 or 8 m (25 ft converted into metric). The scaled contour interval is 14 or 16 mm so a board approximately equal to this dimension should be used.
4 Take care to position each contour accurately. If any excavations are required they should be cut out prior to smoothing out the profile. The best material for completing the relief is a commercial filler such as Tetrion but it is expensive for anything other than the smallest model. Plaster of paris, papier-mâché or any similar material is more than adequate. Take care to work to your contours.

Alternatively, landscapes can be created using cross-sections – wire and plaster bandages – but this requires more skill.

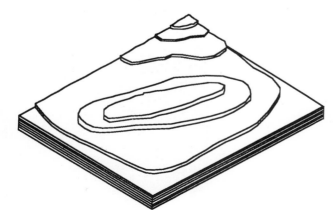

Modelling the building

Paper and card are the cheapest and most versatile medium for making models. Developments can be easily produced and detail can be drawn on directly. Details can also be added to a basic shape. If a more rigid form is required, build the model around a foam core or use foam board or featherboard. (Foam board is foam polystyrene with an ABS skin and featherboard has the same core but is clad with white art board.) Balsa wood is also widely used as is sheet polystyrene for models with a lot of detail. Use whatever materials are at hand provided that they have the strength and are reasonably light.

Tips

- Add all artwork to developments before assembly.
- Keep a photocopy of developments.
- Score all joints before folding to obtain crisp corners.
- Try to construct developments from one piece if possible, including flaps. Always glue flaps inside.
- Cut out all windows and apertures prior to folding and insert transparent material for windows at this stage.
- Always cut out with the finished surface uppermost.
- Form curves in thick card by scoring a series of parallel cuts.
- Include as many clues about scale as possible, e.g. people, cars etc.
- Use custom-made modelling papers to indicate textures such as bricks and tiles. Make sure the correct size is available otherwise you will create a 'doll's house' effect.
- Use available textures as in product modelling. Garnet paper makes good gravel paths; emery cloth is excellent for flat roofs and asphalt. Change the colour and you will change the effect, for example paint an abrasive paper green and it becomes a well-mown lawn.
- Textures can also be created by sprinkling sand, gravels etc. over a glued surface — use your imagination!
- Create water using any transparent or translucent reflective materials.
- Scale trees and bushes can be purchased but they are expensive. Try using foam, twigs, pine cones, oasis (used for flower arranging) or anything which seems suitable. Take a twig from the top of a frequently trimmed privet hedge, dip the ends in glue, coat with sawdust and spray with appropriate colour. This makes a good tree. Hedges are easily made from carved oasis.

Finishing models

Often models are best left in a single uniform colour. This can be achieved by painting with an emulsion paint. Do not add too much detail and keep colours toned down unless you are producing a very precise accurate model.

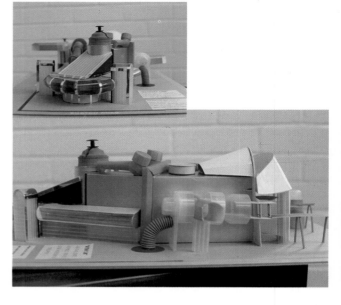

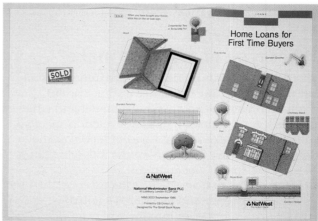

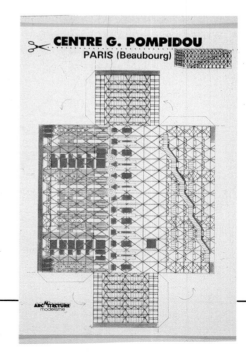

Modelling furniture

A great deal can be learnt from making scale models of furniture before constructing a full-scale prototype. This is true if you are designing a coffee table, chair, or room divider for domestic use, or furniture for a working environment such as a school, hospital, office or factory. Making a prototype is expensive and time-consuming and something you are more likely to do in design and realization. In design and communication designing furniture and making scale models is suitable for both major and minor projects.

Materials

Models can be made out of any suitable material. Balsa wood is quick and easy to work. It can be stained to resemble any type of wood. There are a wide range of tubes available commercially for modelling metal or plastic structures. Any sheet material can be used to represent manufactured boards and perforated metal and plastic are available at about the right scale. Upholstery is easy to model but make sure you use fabric which has a pattern in scale with the model. A wide range of scrap materials can be successfully used such as lollipop sticks, straws, cardboard tubes etc.

Example

The brief was to design a modular furniture system which could be adapted to solve a wide range of storage situations in the home; the maximum versatility should be obtained from the minimum range of components.

The idea being developed is based on tubing and a bolting system for joining verticals to horizontals. The final prototype would be made from tubular steel with shelves of perforated steel sheet. Plastic moulded boxes would clip into the system to hold drawers.

A scale of 1:6 was chosen and suitable plastic tubing obtained. The tube was machined accurately to the correct lengths. Commercial fittings were used for the bends and joints. The boxes were made out of an extruded plastic strip. Shelves and drawers were constructed from perforated plastic and then sprayed.

Once all the components are made, various arrangements can be tried to see how adaptable the design is. Each model is recorded as a photograph. If you can, add some objects similar in scale to the model. This will help improve the degree of realism. Another idea is to create a simple room set, for example a wall which has been papered, as a backdrop.

All the products used in this model are obtainable from EMA model supplies.

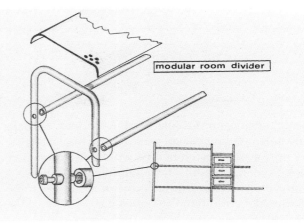

modular room divider

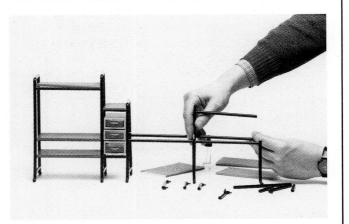

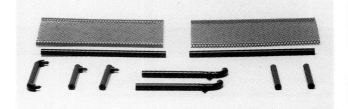

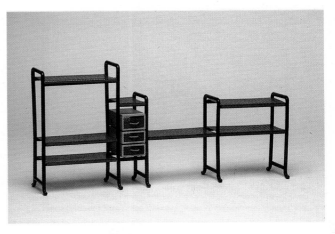

Architectural modelling—examples

The drawings on this page and the models on page 100 illustrate one design project. The brief was to identify a small patch of land within an urban area ripe for development. Once identified, housing appropriate to the area and environment was to be designed. In addition the housing should be thermally efficient to conserve energy.

A small plot of disused allotments was selected in a suburban environment, on an estate composed mainly of bungalows. The site was carefully recorded and ideas generated. You can see from the sketches and drawings how these developed. The plans included a solar heating system employing warm air from the conservatory and its roof. To capitalize on the sun's energy the correct orientation of the buildings was essential. Eventually the plans had advanced sufficiently for a model to be made.

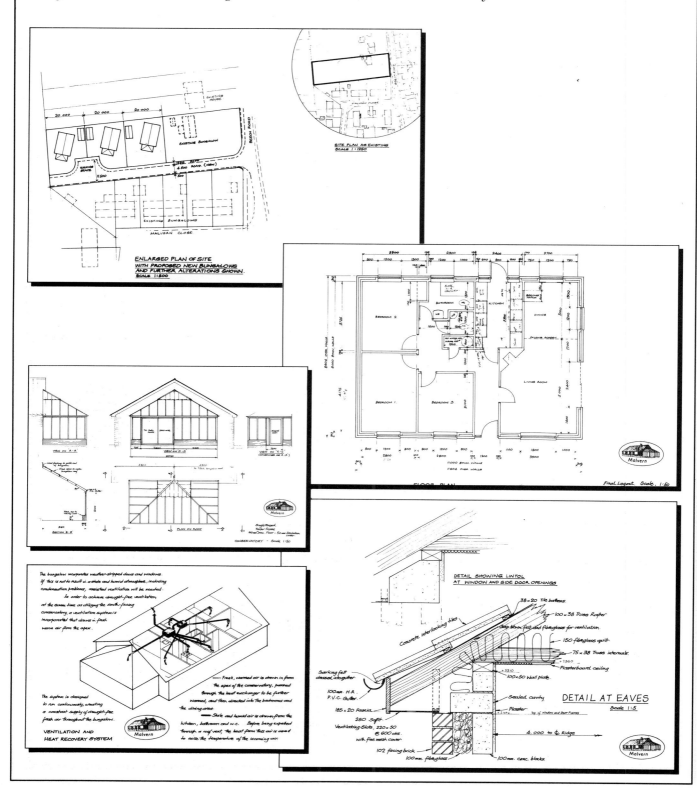

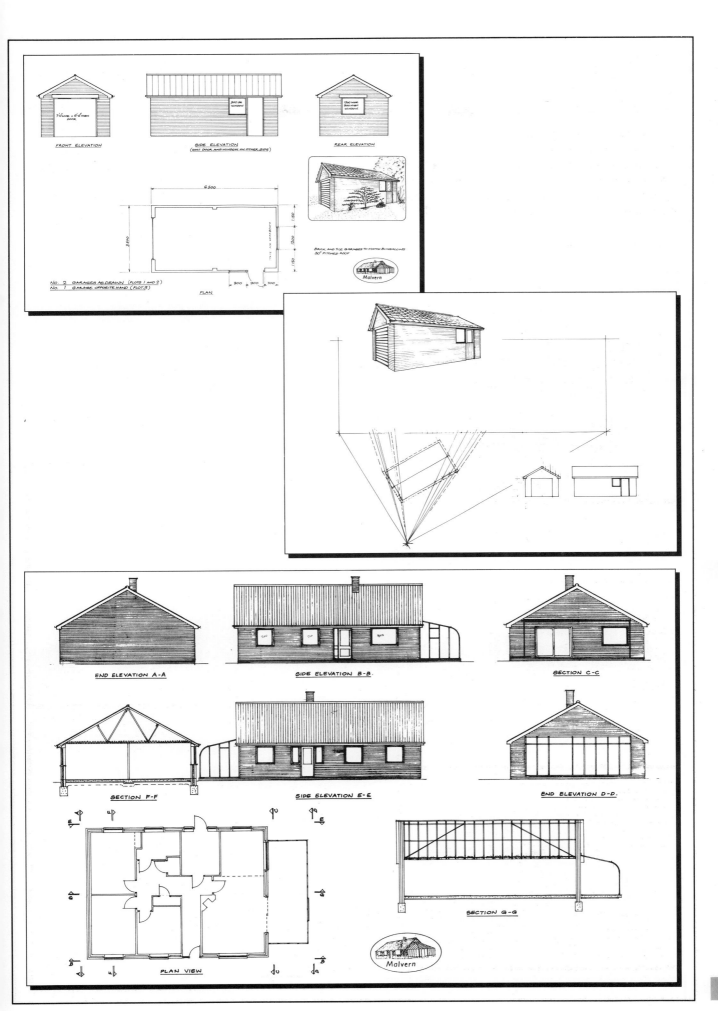

FRONT ELEVATION

SIDE ELEVATION
(CAR DOOR AND WINDOW ON OTHER SIDE)

REAR ELEVATION

PLAN

NO. 2 GARAGES AS DRAWN (PLOTS 1 AND 2)
NO. 1 GARAGE OPPOSITE HAND (PLOT 3)

BRICK AND TILE GARAGES TO MATCH BUNGALOWS
30° PITCHED ROOF

Malvern

END ELEVATION A-A

SIDE ELEVATION B-B.

SECTION C-C

SECTION F-F

SIDE ELEVATION E-E

END ELEVATION D-D.

PLAN VIEW

SECTION G-G

Malvern

99

The first model was a site model. This showed how the three bungalows would occupy the land. It could also have shown how access to garages etc. would be achieved and how services would reach the buildings. The next model, on a much larger scale, was of one of the bungalows. Every aspect of the design has been taken into account. In particular the heating system has been modelled to explain how solar energy will be incorporated. The final design element of the project was to design a brochure for the estate agent to give to possible purchasers.

THE MALVERN
Rushmere St.Andrew

ESTATE AGENT
O. SALTER FRICS
The Walk, Kesgrove.
tel: Ipswich 625 089

ARCHITECT – J. HUNTER FRIBA
Studio 4, Redisham.
tel: Beccles 715 234

Activity 98*

Select one of the following situations. Design and then model, to an appropriate scale, your solution.

1 *A new enclosed porch to your home.*
2 *A new garage for your parents' car to include a workshop area.*
3 *A conservatory to be attached to your home.*
4 *An extension to your home or a neighbour's, to meet a particular need which they have identified.*

Modelling furniture – examples

On this page there are some examples of furniture models. The first is a view of the storage system described on page 97. The other examples illustrate a variety of stages in a range of design briefs. They are concerned with folding structures, specialized school furniture and domestic furniture.

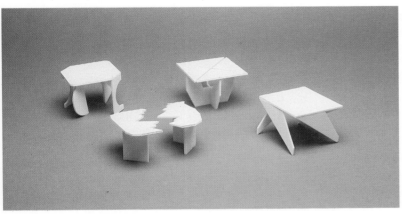

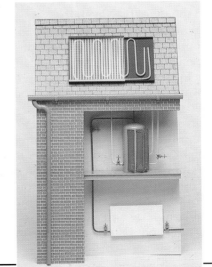

described on page 97.

Activity 99

Design a chair which, when not in use, can be folded and hung on the wall to create a piece of two-dimensional sculpture. Model your design at one-quarter life size.

EQUIPMENT

The photocopier

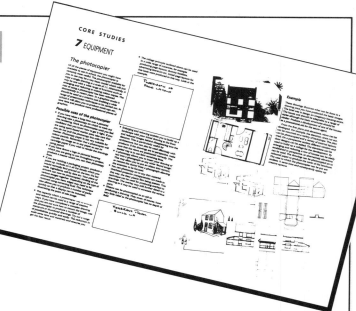

Of all the pieces of equipment you might have available to use in school, the photocopier is certainly most useful. The photocopier available for you to use may be a very basic model which will just copy a single drawing at a scale of 1:1. Alternatively, it may be one with a wide range of functions such as enlarging and reducing or making colour copies. The cost of using a photocopier has been reduced dramatically in recent years. In a graphics studio it should be used as a creative tool enabling a wide range of presentation techniques to be carried out. In school it will allow you to produce mock-ups etc., save time and produce more professional pieces of graphics.

Possible uses of the photocopier

- If you have taken a long time over a pictorial drawing take a photocopy on which to work out the rendering. Work on photocopies until you feel confident that you know how to get it right. If you are using spirit-based marker pens take care that you do not pull the photocopy line with the marker. Photocopy paper is not very suitable for colour pencils. Remember that a photocopier will transfer the image on to any paper so use A4 cartridge paper if you wish to render the drawings using pencil.

- If you have drawn a logo or pictorial lettering which you are going to use throughout a project, produce a master which you can then photocopy from.

- If you are tackling a packaging project, produce a paste-up. Include on it all the details which you would normally find printed on the box; the bar code, ingredients, sell-by date etc. Your piece of artwork can now be photocopied, binding all the various images together. Depending on the type of photocopier you have, edges may need to be removed using correcting fluid. This technique also allows you to produce a number of packs quickly so that a display can be mounted, illustrating the point of sale image.

- The collage principle outlined above can be used in a wide range of instances, for example producing page layouts, dummy booklets, advertising literature etc. Initial page layouts for this book were produced in this way. Look at the example.

- The capacity which a photocopier has to enlarge and reduce can be used in a range of creative ways. If you have completed a complex drawing and you are not sure how to mount the image, use the photocopier to produce a number of miniature or thumbnail drawings. Try out a range of possibilities quickly and easily. The reduction in scale saves time and materials and ensures you get the best result.

- Enlarging and reducing enables you to build up a landscape with your initial drawing at the front and reduced images behind disappearing into the distance. This is particularly useful for architecture, but can also be used effectively with products. If the drawings are in perspective, make sure that the views are positioned correctly. The easiest way is to use feint vanishing lines.

- A photocopy allows you to insert your drawing or text into a photograph or any other 'found image'. This may allow you to put an object into context, or remove the clutter from a photograph allowing the attention to be focused.

- You can photocopy on to any thin material. Overhead projector transparencies are made in this way, the clear plastic film being acetate. This technique can be used for producing overlays to drawings. The overlay may add further detail to a drawing or it may be used to annotate the various parts.

- Objects can be photocopied as an aid to producing a drawing. They must, of course, have very little relief as the photocopier has no depth of field.

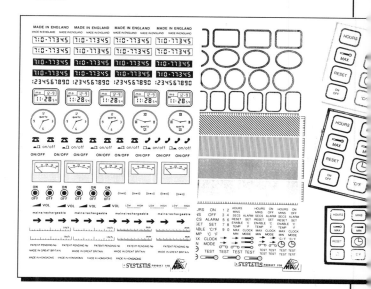

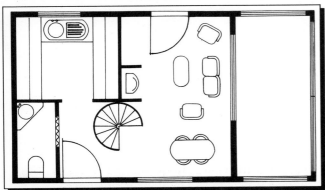

Example

These drawings illustrate what can be done to a drawing once you have produced the basic images. The brief was to design an imaginary housing estate. The house unit should be adaptable to a range of styles although the basic structures should be similar. Produce a development of one of the houses as a promotional aid for the estate agent.

From the first plans and elevations, views can be developed. For example, the elevation, once cut out, can be mounted on a variety of backdrops. The plan can be photocopied and a variety of internal layouts tried. On a perspective outline different window and door designs can be added. The elevations can be used to build up a collage for the development. By enlarging and reducing, a row of houses can be easily established in perspective, or alternatively elevations can be used. The drawings can be photocopied on to coloured paper to produce the cover of the brochure. The uses to which the photocopier can be put are endless. It saves time and consequently opens up creative options.

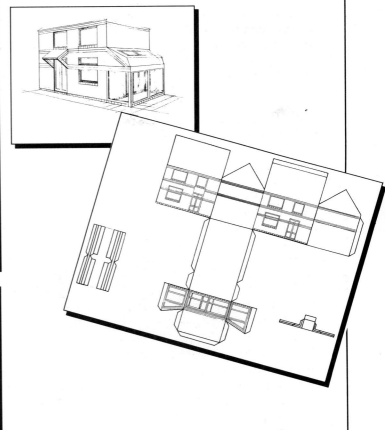

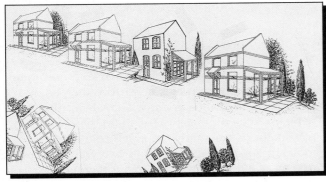

The Letrajet

It is possible to turn your marker pens into devices which will spray the media on to your artwork. This is done by pointing a jet of air on to the nib of the pen which makes it behave a bit like an airbrush. A commercial version is made by Letraset and is called a Letrajet. It will only work with Letraset fine-line Pantone pens. It has some real advantages over an airbrush, but of course there are disadvantages as well.

Advantages

- It is very easy to change from one colour to another: simply change the pen.
- Initially it is cheaper to buy and easier to control than an airbrush.
- Spray work can blend with and perfectly match graphics produced with a marker.

Disadvantages

- The action is essentially on/off, making it difficult to achieve the effects possible with an airbrush.
- You cannot mix your own particular colours. You require a different pen for each colour, which can prove expensive.

A Letrajet will, like an airbrush, need an air supply. A compressor with a pressure regulator is the best system but it is expensive initially. Canned air can also be purchased, but although cheap in the first instance, the cost quickly builds up. It is possible to improvise — all you need is a reservoir and a pump. A foot pump and car tyre, or alternatively a gardener's killer spray, will work. You will have to make an adaptor to connect your Letrajet to your air supply.

Getting started

You will quickly discover that the key to any accurate spray work is careful masking. Low tack masking film is expensive and requires a degree of skill to use. Paper masks can be used, the only problem being that the paper must be weighted down to prevent it blowing away in the air stream. A sheet of tin plate and a number of small magnets will quickly solve the the problem. Look at the photograph and you will see how secure masking can be achieved. Quite complex work can be carried out using this system.

Try the following to help you master this type of spray system. Before you start make sure you are holding it comfortably with your forefinger on the control. Make sure the airline is free and will not catch on anything, jolting your arm.

1 Start by drawing lines. The distance of the nib from the paper will determine the thickness of the line. The closer the nib the narrower and more dense the line will be. The further away, the fuzzier and more diffused the line will become. The speed with which you move your hand will also affect the density. Your attempts will look far better if you spray through a square mask.

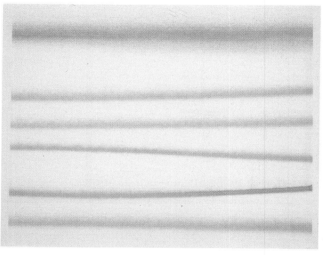

2 Try spraying a series of spots. Vary the size by varying the distance from the paper. Small precise spots are by far the most difficult.

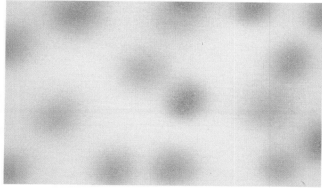

3 With a square mask try to lay down an even square of colour. A golden rule is never turn the pen over your artwork. If you do you will create a splodge which is difficult to get rid of. Build the colour gradually, do not apply too much colour too quickly. You will be surprised when you remove the mask at how dense the colour patch is.

4 Using a similar square mask try creating a **vignette** — a graded tone, from a very pale colour at the top of the square to a dense tone at the bottom. Remember the density of tone can be decreased by increasing the distance between the pen nib and the paper. Try working from dark to light and then light to dark. Which direction gives you the best results?

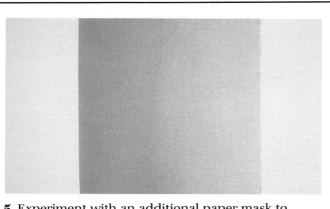

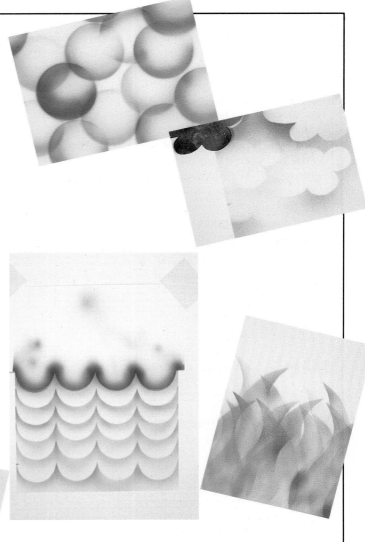

5 Experiment with an additional paper mask to create striped and square patterns. The examples give you an idea of what can be done.

Once you have had a go at these simple exercises you should attempt rendering a drawing. The example shown here is a rough or scamp from a perfume advert. Follow through the stages to see how it has been achieved. Remember elements can be sprayed separately and then assembled. This **collage** technique is very useful in an example like this one as the bottle can be tried against a number of different backdrops. Once the Letrajet has been used the edges can be tidied up using coloured pencils and highlights and details added.

It is not very difficult to make your own sprayhead. All you require is a fine nozzle held at the correct angle for a particular marker pen, and an air control system — a simple valve. The photographs show some home-made versions. One is an improved version. It has been carefully engineered so that the air control is variable. The others work on much cheaper, water-based pens. They use a range of objects, such as the nib from a biro with the tungsten ball removed. They only have a simple on/off control. As you can see it is possible to make your own system. It is also possible to make a system which works using a technical pen. You may have to experiment to discover the correct pen size, but once you do it will work very efficiently.

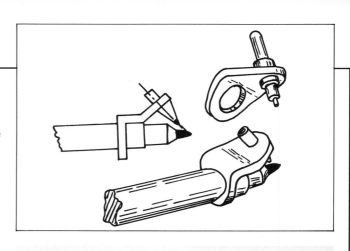

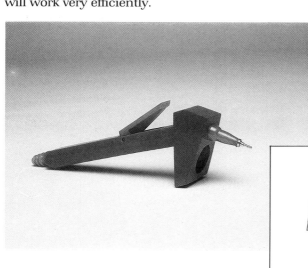

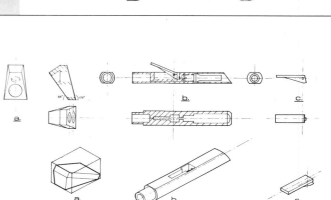

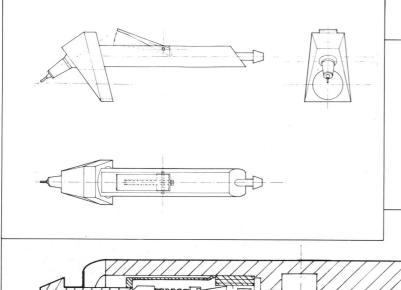

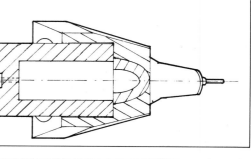

The airbrush

There is a range of ways in which media can be sprayed on to a piece of artwork, but the most sophisticated is the airbrush. Its invention is credited to Charles L. Burdick. He called his invention the Aerograph and in 1893 he set up the Fountain Brush Company in Clerkenwell Green, London to manufacture it. Other companies also started manufacture and a number of developments took place. Since 1931, when suction feed brushes were introduced, the device has remained largely unaltered.

Airbrushing is an expensive technique. There are two basic pieces of equipment — the brush and a compressor. In addition, there are consumables — masking film, media to be sprayed, inks etc., and good quality papers and boards.

How it works

The airbrush directs a flow of air through a nozzle. A needle is located in the nozzle along which pigment flows. The action of operating the brush pulls the needle back creating a gap between the needle and the nozzle. As a result the air and the pigment mix causing the pigment to break into very fine droplets — an **aerosol**. The density of the resulting spray depends on the balance of air and pigment, the distance from the paper and the angle of the airbrush.

Two types

Basically there are two types:
- Single action — in this type of airbrush the paint flow and air supply are controlled separately. Most commonly the paint flow is set by a screw thread at the back of the airbrush. The finger control, used when operating the airbrush, controls the air flow.
- Double action — in this type the paint and air are controlled from a single finger control. Typically, the finger pushes down for air and pulls back for paint.

Check the manufacturer's information before starting to use an airbrush. Check the recommended air pressure, usually between 30 and 40 psi.

Initial exercises

Make sure that you are holding the airbrush comfortably. Hold it between your thumb and index finger, which is used to operate the finger lever. Make sure the airline is free and does not constrain the movement of your hand. Start by just getting the feel of the airbrush. Try varying the distance from the nozzle to the paper and its angle. Start by drawing lines. Notice how the distance from the paper determines the width of the line. Try writing your name.

Next try laying down an even square of media, using a paper mask. Using the same mask try a graduated tone. With paper masks of a rectangle, triangle and cone have a go at producing a cylinder, cone and sphere.

Simple masking

Try creating some patterned surfaces using a strip of paper. A straight edge used in two different directions will produce a quilted effect. Try other profiles and see what you can produce.

A five-pointed star is a simple geometric shape which can be rendered using paper templates. Always start by doing a simple pencil sketch of what you are attempting to produce. Then follow these steps:

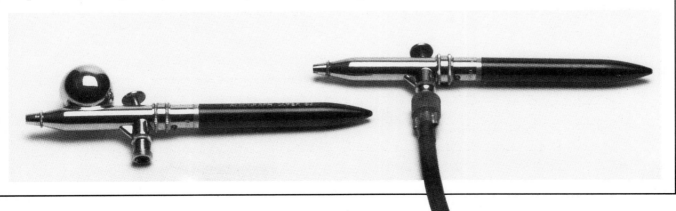

1 Cut out accurately the paper mask of the star. Place it in the correct position. Spray a very light tint all over the whole area.
2 With a paper mask of the shape shown, spray each arm as indicated by your sketch. This creates the ridge along each arm.
3 Finally use the second mask to produce the valley between each arm. The star is now complete.

Masking with film

Low tack masking film or Frisk film as it is often called is essential for detailed airbrush work. The film should be capable of being laid down on paper and card, adhering to it and then being removed without damaging the surface of the paper. Always check that the film does not damage the surface before starting on a complex piece of work. Always use a sharp knife for cutting film; a scalpel is best. The knife should cut the film without any pressure being exerted as this is likely to mark the artwork.

Example: masking using film

This example illustrates the stages in airbrushing a bolt. Follow the stages from the photographs. The drawing is carefully copied or traced on to the board or paper on which you are going to work. Use a piece of layout paper or something similar as a primary mask. Cut a window which exposes the line drawing. Now lay masking film over this area. Take great care that it does not wrinkle and that there are no bubbles. Smooth it down gently but do not press too hard. Cut out the first areas to be airbrushed. Remove each in turn and airbrush them with the required tones. Do not replace the film until you are certain that the ink is dry. After all the areas have been rendered go back and add the shadows. This may mean using a fresh sheet of film.

The key to airbrushing is accurate masking and patience. Take great care of the airbrush as it is an extremely precise tool. Always clean it carefully and use it as you are shown. Below there are some examples of what professionals can do with an airbrush. As you can see the results are larger than life, better than a photograph!

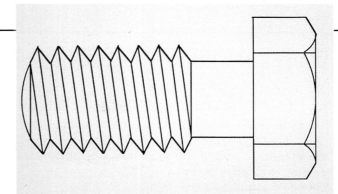

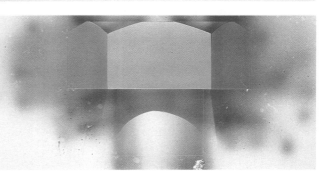

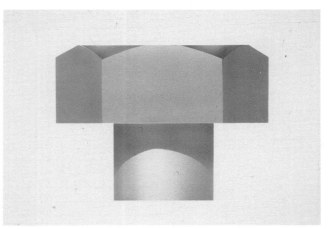

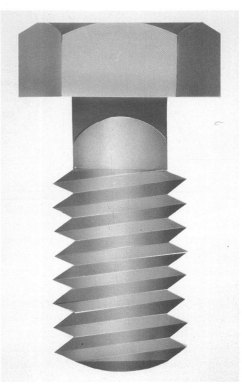

Enlargement and reduction

There are many reasons why you might need to either enlarge or reduce a drawing. One of the most important is to enable you to include the maximum amount of detail on a drawing. The quality of any drawing can be improved dramatically if it is reduced. Enlarging often has the opposite effect. When preparing paste-ups or exhibition panels, visual images frequently have to be scaled to fit in the appropriate space.

There are a variety of ways in which drawings can be enlarged and reduced. You are already familiar with some of these. The grid method which you learnt first does not involve the use of any equipment; it is simple but very effective. The **pantograph** has some advantages but can be awkward to use. It can be easily made from scrap material.

The **photocopier** can be very useful (see page 102). The majority of copiers only enlarge or reduce by standard proportions, a reduction from A3 to A4 (71 per cent) being one of the most common. Most machines can reduce but fewer can enlarge. Only the most expensive machines allow you to determine the exact proportion of enlargement or reduction you require. These copiers will become more common as their relative price drops. The other problem with photocopiers is that they always produce a black image, which will smudge when worked over with a spirit marker.

The visualizer

This machine is like a sophisticated light box. It works indirectly in that the image is first produced on tracing or see-through paper and then transferred on to the finished medium. The visualizer is an invaluable machine to the designer — most studios have one. They are beginning to be found in schools and will become more common in the future. They are easy to operate and enable an image to be reduced or enlarged to exactly the required size. It is also possible to place three-dimensional objects on the copyboard or table and produce a drawing of them. Although the depth of field is limited, it does allow outline drawings to be produced, especially orthographic views.

How it works

The image (artwork or object to be drawn) is placed on the copyboard which is beneath the lens and viewing screen. The image can be lit from either above or below, as is the case when working from transparencies. The amount of enlargement is controlled by two handles. One moves the lens and the other the copyboard. On some visualizers the copying surface is fixed and the handles give a coarse and fine adjustment.

The image is projected on to tracing or layout paper which is placed on the glass viewing screen. The viewing area is hooded, but even so it is best to site a visualizer in a darkened corner. Alternatively, have a blanket available to throw over the front of the hood to help cut down the light. Always make sure that the master image and copy are taped down so that no movement occurs during the operation. Using this method it is possible to produce a drawing in whichever medium you choose — coloured pencil, technical pen etc.

The optiscope

This is a direct projector. That means the image is projected directly on to the required surface. Optiscopes are extremely precise, having a very good quality lens system. They are used by a variety of designers, especially graphic designers and illustrators. They are also used by signwriters when painting logos and company names on to lorries, tankers and aircraft.

How it works

The image to be copied is placed on the copyboard or stand. It is lit from the front by tungsten halogen bulbs which give off a great deal of heat as well as light. The image is then directed through a lens and mirror system on to the chosen drawing surface. The projector is focused by moving the projecting head up and down. The head can also be swivelled so that the image can be projected horizontally as well as vertically.

It is extremely important that the drawing surface is rigid as any movement can cause difficult realignment problems. The biggest drawback with the optiscope is that your drawing hand interferes with the image being projected, and this takes some getting used to.

Alternatives

In school, if you do not have the equipment described above, there are a number of alternatives. However, they can only be used to enlarge images.
1 The **episcope** is a projector which is used for enlarging books and maps. It can be used by projecting images on to a wall.
2 **Slide projectors** are capable of huge enlargement whilst retaining a great amount of detail. This is a lengthy process, as a slide has to be taken first.

Many professionals work from slides, especially if they are producing a very high quality piece of graphics, for example of a sports car.
3 **Overhead projectors** can be used if the image is on acetate or film. Drawing on acetate is best achieved by using a needle with a cork as a handle. This is, however, a lengthy procedure. It can be useful when painting scenery or producing large posters. In these cases it is best to make an overhead projector transparency of the original artwork using a photocopier. This system can also be used for combining more than one image and for investigating possible combinations.

The copy or process camera

The correct name of this camera is a **photo mechanical transfer (PMT) camera**. It is an expensive piece of equipment, used primarily by graphic designers. It produces perfect enlarged or reduced images as well as a wide range of variations. The quality of the images it produces is often better than the original as it can increase density and remove imperfections such as the edge line from several images on a paste-up. Printers use this camera to **screen** images. This is the term used to describe the reduction of a continuous tone image to thousands of dots. The screen used will determine the size and number of the dots. These images are often called halftones, and a printer works from them.

Examine a page of print under a magnifying glass and you will see that it is made up of thousands of dots. Colour printing is done in exactly the same way. A full colour image is produced from just four colours — black, cyan, magenta and yellow. If you examine a cardboard box such as one for breakfast cereal you will find on one of the flaps a colour bar which indicates the colours which have been used in the printing process. Cut down on the colours and the cost of printing is reduced. All colours can be produced from the three primaries plus black.

The camera

There is a wide range of cameras, which use a variety of films. There are instant cameras, single lens reflex cameras and polaroid cameras. You will have to work with the equipment available to you. You may work in black and white or colour prints, or colour transparencies; it will depend on exactly what you are trying to achieve. The camera is a valuable tool for the designer as it has a number of uses:

- For research — often when you are out on location gathering information for a design project you have to work quickly. There is insufficient time to sketch and draw. The camera allows you to record images quickly. The photographs can then be analysed back in the studio when there is more time and less pressure.
- For recording — there are many occasions when it is important to record how something was produced. A camera allows every stage to be recorded for future reference.
- For increasing realism — often the end result of a design project is a model. A photograph of the model, in context, will often enhance the illusion. A model of any product photographed as if in use, such as a hairdryer, calculator or glue gun, will be more convincing, especially if a few tricks are employed. If the model hairdryer is photographed in use and out of shot a real hairdryer is being used to blow the hair, or glue is seen to be dripping from the nozzle of a model glue gun, the model will look like the real thing. In the case of scale models, such as those employed in architecture, the camera is used to make the model appear life-size. A modelscope (like a periscope but used for looking into a model) can be attached to a camera so that street level shots can be taken.
- For super realistic graphics — often in advertising or promotional graphics — an image is required which is larger than life. The graphic artist will often start from a photograph of the object shot under controlled lighting conditions. The resulting photograph, with reflections and highlights, will be broken down into its many elements and then redrawn and rendered with enhanced realism. See if you can spot any images which you think may have been produced in this way.

- For creating atmosphere or environment — how often do we look at a photograph and think it was shot in some exotic location, when in fact it was taken in a studio? This can be easily done with just a few carefully chosen props. This has been done in this advertising photograph for a perfume. Some sand and a miniature pyramid complete the illusion. Because we believe what we see, the camera can fool our eyes, as in the example shown. The effect was achieved by sticking the bottle to a base board and taking the shot with the bottle on its side.

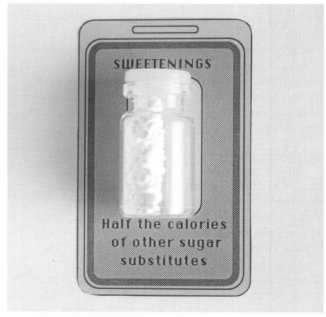

THE FILM BASE IS COATED WITH GRAINS OF **SILVER** HELD IN AN **EMULSION**

WHEN **EXPOSED** TO LIGHT THE SILVER DARKENS

DEVELOPMENT MULTIPLIES THIS DARKENING MILLIONS OF TIMES....

......AND PRODUCES A **NEGATIVE** IN WHICH THE TONES ARE REVERSED.

PASSING LIGHT THROUGH THE **NEGATIVE** ONTO ANOTHER SILVER **EMULSION** NOW ON A PAPER BASE

DEVELOPMENT NOW PRODUCES AN OPPOSITE EFFECT.......

..... A **POSITIVE PRINT.**

- For presentations — colour slides are an excellent medium for making a presentation. The images need to be carefully chosen as they must maintain interest for a number of seconds. Professional presentations often use split screens to create multi-images. However, this requires several projectors and electronic synchronization. This type of slide presentation is often used at a product launch or a sales conference. It can quickly establish a message or identity in the minds of the audience. If you wish to produce a slide presentation (and given the right brief it would be a very suitable project) the first step is to produce a storyboard. This is a shot by shot plan of the presentation — a series of sketch images relating to each photograph in the presentation. You must plan and design every aspect, including title shots and commentary, before you start any location shooting.

Photograms

Photograms are a bit like shadow photographs. They are made by placing objects on to a sheet of light-sensitive paper and exposing them to light. The process can be used for making striking covers for reports and design folders. Once exposed the print is developed in the same way as photographic prints.

A range of interesting results can be achieved by varying the light and using reflective objects to produce spots and lines of light. All-over patterns can be produced using net or sawdust, for example.

Build up the image on a sheet of glass which is then placed on the photographic paper. Lettering can be added in the same way by using rub-down letters on glass or clear film: This will produce white letters on a black background which appears very striking.

DESIGN *in action*

TITLE

5 seconds & fade /////

CAR SHOT ←

Fade in — 2 secs sound over — cut "DESIGN IS.....

AIROPLANE →

Cut — 2 secs sound over — cut ..... ALL AROUND...

YATCH ←

Cut — 2 secs sound over — cut ..... US."

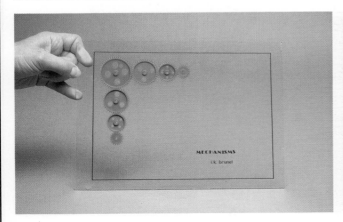

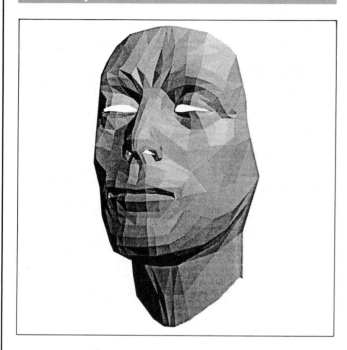

The microcomputer

In design and communication the micro has several uses. The most obvious is computer graphics, using the computer as a tool to generate visual images. Another important use is as a word processor. This is helpful when writing project reports. An advanced form of word processing is the use of the computer as a desktop publishing centre. High quality graphics can be produced without a single paste-up. Information can be stored and easily retrieved using a data base which is essentially an electronic filing cabinet.

What you can produce using a computer will depend on the systems and software you have available. This varies from school to school. It will also depend on your ability to operate the various systems. If you also take computer studies or business studies, for example, you will be able to use the expertise you have acquired in design and communication.

The computer is playing an increasingly important role in the design world. It is not restricted to any particular area but permeates all aspects. **Computer aided engineering (CAE)** is a term which embraces both **computer aided design (CAD)** and **computer aided manufacture (CAM)**. In CAD the model which has been generated on the screen and stored in the computer's memory is the object which is being designed. The designer is able to communicate with the computer to manipulate the model in a variety of ways. The car designer may wish to rotate the three-dimensional view of a car body, to view it from various angles, whereas the designer of electronic circuits might wish to examine the waveforms produced by a circuit. The architect or interior designer may have a library of components or fittings which can be assembled on screen to design buildings or room layouts.

Once the model has been designed using the computer it can be used as the blueprint for manufacture. The CAM facility may be directly linked and components can be produced automatically. This is becoming commonplace in engineering and the automobile industry. Quite often, no drawing or hard copy is even produced. The design is stored digitally and only viewed on a visual display unit (VDU). In other fields of design, such as architecture, large plotting machines are used to produce the vast quantity of plans and elevations which will be required by the building contractor.

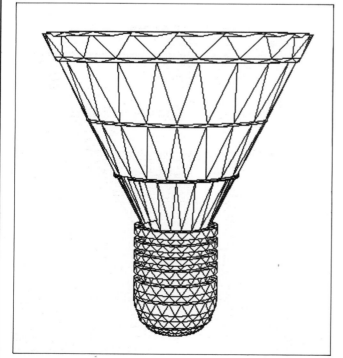

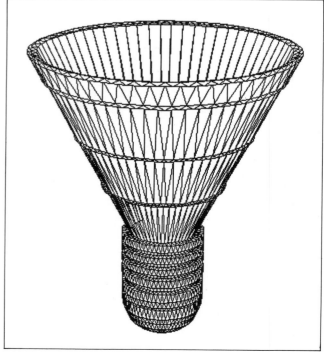

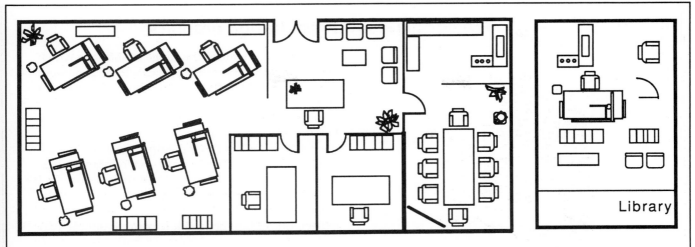

Library

Software

You are probably familiar with much of the terminology related to computers. Generally speaking the hardware system will not operate without software. There are three broad types of software:

- System software — this is usually supplied by the manufacturer.
  It consists of:
  1 The programming languages such as BASIC or Pascal.
  2 An operating system which might, for example, include input and file handling routines.
  3 Programs for the control of the interface between the computer and external devices such as other terminals.

- Utilities — these are the programs which carry out functions which are common to most users, such as copying or dumping data from one medium to another, e.g. disc to VDU or VDU to printer.

- Application software — this type of software does not usually come with a system. It is purchased so that the computer can carry out the particular tasks which you require of it. You may write the software yourself, but this is unlikely. The system at school will probably have software of this type which fits one of the categories which we shall look at in more detail.

Another important aspect of computer graphics is in animation. From full-length movie films to the title sequence for TV shows and advertisements, computer animation has been growing rapidly as ever more sophisticated images become possible. The day is rapidly coming when it will be difficult to tell the computer generated images from the real thing! It is impossible in a book of this nature to deal in detail with every aspect of this field. All that can be done is to show how you might capitalize on the power of the computer within design and communication. Whichever project you select, there is bound to be some way in which you can make the computer work for you.

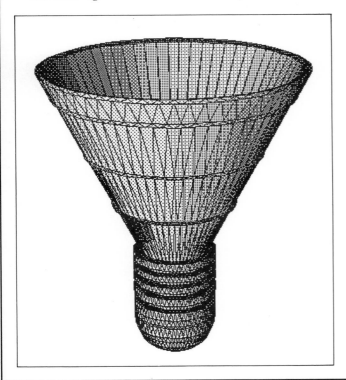

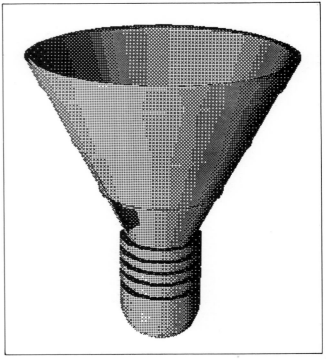

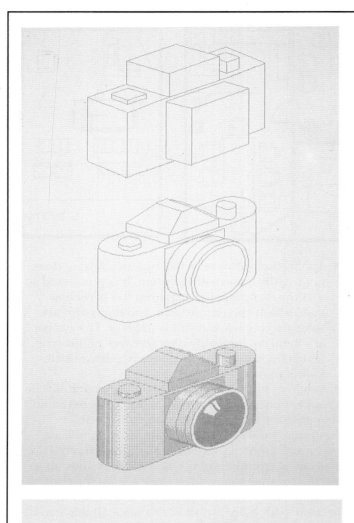

Presentation graphics

This category includes the range of software which allows pictorial and artistic images to be generated. They are often referred to as **painting** or **art systems** and operate in colour. The number and mix of colours is dependent on the power of the computer. Painting systems are generally screen based. This means they control the individual pixels on the screen. The resolution of such systems can only be increased by storing screens on disc. It is now possible to get good-quality colour hard copy from these programs. A dot-matrix printer with a four-colour ribbon or an ink-jet printer are the two common systems which you will find in school.

These programs invariably use a mouse as the inputting device. The mouse controls the movement of the cursor around the screen. The screen display is what is known as a WIMP environment. This stands for windows, icons, menus and pointer routines, all of which are available via the mouse controller.

Software available for school has the following features:

- Toolbox — usually displayed on screen, this contains all the primary drawing tools such as pencil, spray, eraser, flood fill, text and line, box, circle and ellipse drawing routines.
- Pattern boxes — a window which enables colour selection and shows the range of patterns which can be selected. It is usually possible to create your own patterns. The patterns may be simple repetitive images such as brick or tile patterns, or alternatively they could be specific symbols. Symbols are usually referred to as icons. They could be electrical symbols or those used on weather maps as shown here.
- Usually operational commands are available via the pull-down menus at the top of the screen.

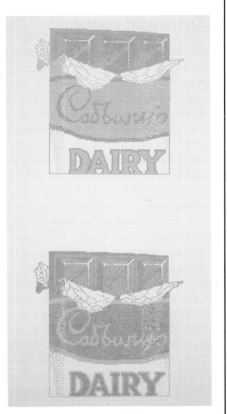

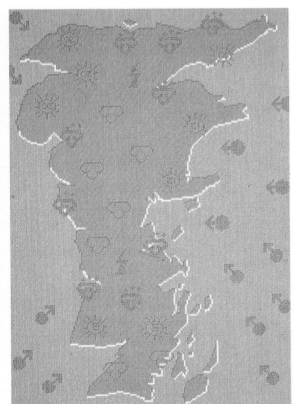

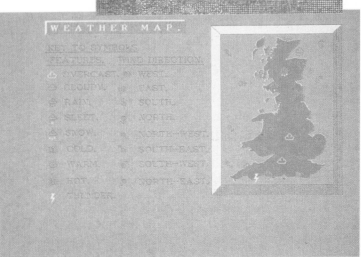

Technical graphics

Within this category we shall include orthographic and working drawings, formalized technical drawings which describe the precise shape and size of an object. Traditionally these have been produced by draughtspeople, but now software makes it possible to carry out the complete range of technical graphics on the computer. It is possible to do the same kind of drawings on the microcomputer which will be available to you. Initially it may seem a laborious process, but in the long run there are many advantages. In industry, where a design office or company is using the same system, productivity is increased dramatically. Drawings are produced more quickly (lead times are shortened); when a design is updated the drawings are easily modified; and the accuracy of drawings is improved and so consequently is that of the product.

Software now available for the school market has the following features:

- The best systems operate in the same way as professional CAD systems, by storing the coordinates of the lines and arcs. This means that the VDU is merely a window on to a much larger drawing board which can be moved under this window.
- Macros, often called layers or elements, can be created. These can be built up to form a much larger drawing. Individual macros can be manipulated in the following ways: reduced or enlarged, moved, repeated, rotated and reflected. These enable components with a number of identical parts to be drawn quickly, for example nuts and bolts on a coupling flange or windows in a building.
- Libraries can be compiled of standard drawings or conventions, electronic or hydraulic symbols, borders and title blocks etc.
- Hatching, dimensioning and text can often be added automatically.
- Zooming, scaling and pen facilities are available.

As you can imagine, this range of features enable complex drawings to be produced quickly and plotted accurately, once you have mastered the system.

Three-dimensional modelling programs

This type of program enables a three-dimensional view of an object to be revolved on screen in real time. It requires a very powerful computer, and even so it can be very time consuming to give the computer the initial information. Each point on the object has to be described three-dimensionally (x, y and z coordinates). As more powerful systems become available in school this type of modelling will be very useful. It will enable animation to be more realistic.

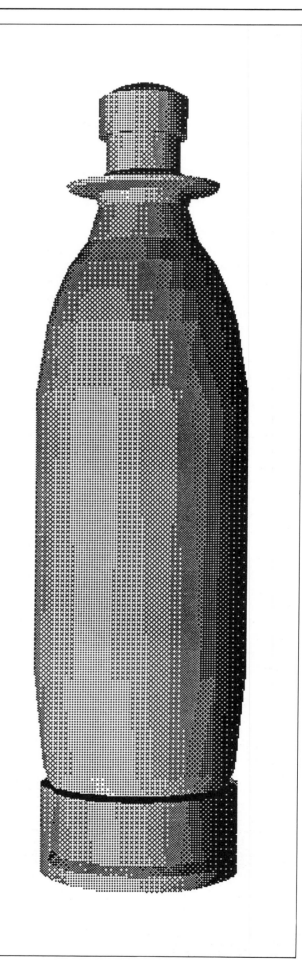

Desktop publishing

This is a specialized type of software which enables graphic images and text to be combined. It is used to produce pages for a book or magazine, information leaflets, etc. It allows the images to be manipulated to produce the desired layout. The designer can try a variety of paste-ups, each being saved on disc. A very sophisticated program will then allow you to view all the possible designs before making a selection. It usually allows a wide range of type fonts to be selected in a range of point sizes and styles.

Business graphics

There is a range of software which can be grouped under this heading.

1 Word processing — all computers have the capability to manipulate text. This allows text to be formatted, justified, and edited, amongst many other facilities, before being printed. A daisy-wheel or laser printer produces the best result, but frequently in school only a dot-matrix printer is available. This is suitable for graphic dumps, but will only produce NLQ (near letter quality) text. It is worth producing word processed text as it will look far more professional.

2 Spreadsheets — a spreadsheet is a very useful device for keeping a record of anything which varies, such as salaries in a company, membership of an organization or your own personal finances. It consists of a number of pigeon holes, or slots, each may contain one of the following:

- A number.
- A formula (which is in terms of other slots).
- A label such as TOTAL or INCOME.

   Slots may be linked with other slots so that they may interact with each other across the length or breadth of a sheet. The formula in a slot may, for example, ask it to total all the values in a column. If one of these values changes, the total is automatically adjusted.

   Spreadsheets are widely used in commerce, industry and research, for recording and analysing data, as a step to forecasting and planning.

3 Business graphics — the charts and diagrams in Unit 5 can all be produced using specialized programs. Very few programs allow flair and imagination to be incorporated into the charts.

If you have the opportunity, look for ways in which you can use computers as a tool to help you communicate ideas more efficiently and accurately.

Computer project

John wanted to undertake a project which would use every aspect of the computer, to get as near as he could to a fully integrated CAD-CAM process. The facilities available consisted of BBC Master computers, Boxford CNC lathes and mills, and a range of software. The main problem was what could be achieved given the resources available. John was also keen that the end product might be something that could be produced in quantity to justify the processes. He concluded that he would design and manufacture a product that could be injection moulded, and that the dies would be machined using the CNC mill.

The scale of the product would have to be small because of the limited capacity of the injection moulder. John decided on a promotional key tag. He started the design process using a painting system to design the key tag. There were severe limitations as the end product, which would be moulded, could only be a single colour. Once the form of the tag had been determined he moved on to a draughting package to produce a detailed working drawing of the object and the moulds.

The design confirmed, programming could now start on the mill. The shapes were initially checked out by cutting in acrylic before moving on to aluminium. Once the moulds were complete, trial mouldings were produced with a simple hand-operated home-made moulder. The final stage was to produce the packaging. A blister pack seemed the simplest solution, so the backing board was designed using the painting program, and printed in colour. It was designed using three-colour printing to reduce costs. You can see the final result. John has gone from origination to completion without a pencil touching paper — well hardly!

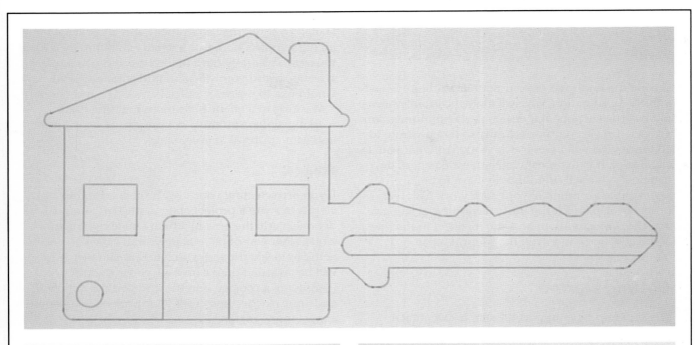

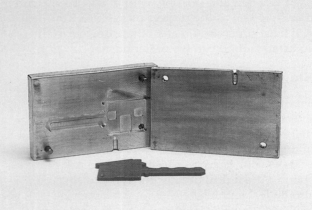

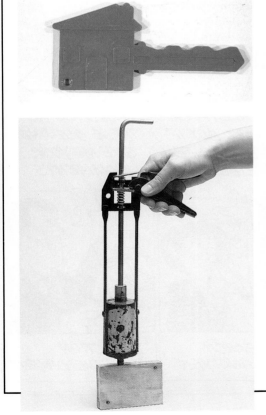

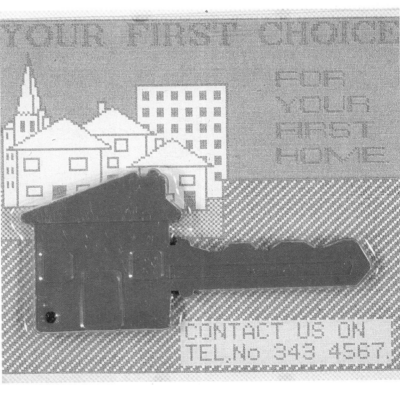

PROJECT AREAS

Selecting projects

During the final year of your course, leading towards a GCSE examination, you will almost certainly have to undertake a personal design and communication project. This is your opportunity to demonstrate to all those who will assess your work just what you are capable of. It is the most challenging aspect of the course as you will undoubtedly have to be responsible for much of your own work. You will probably also find it the most rewarding. It will give you the opportunity to become involved in the part of the syllabus which you have found most interesting.

Getting started

The first and most important step is selecting a project. This will be done in discussion with your class teacher, and possibly with other people who may help you as the project progresses. Your teacher will have supervised many other projects in the past so listen carefully to his or her advice.

Stage 1

Select the area or brief in which you are most interested. Some examination boards allow you to determine your project brief; others will publish a list of titles each year and you will be asked to select one.

Make your decision carefully as you will have to spend a great deal of time on your project. You should feel enthusiastic about what you select. If you can't wait to get started you have probably chosen well. If not, it might be worth thinking again!

Many of the best projects are those where you have a real client, someone who actually has a need which must be met, for example the redesign of a neighbour's garden, plans for a carport, corporate identity for a club or sports team, an instruction leaflet for some new equipment, direction signs for an old people's home, or a small exhibition for a local museum. You only have to look around you and ask questions, and you will soon find someone who would like to use your skills, knowledge and talent.

Working to a client is far more exacting than working alone. You must communicate your ideas and gain approval at every stage.

Stage 2

If you are selecting your own project area your next step is to write a project statement. This should define clearly the area in which you are going to work, what you hope to achieve and how you are going to tackle the task you have set yourself. You will be awarded marks on how you set about identifying a project. If in the end you draw a blank and your teacher has to set your project, you cannot expect many marks.

Stage 3

Once your project statement has been approved think carefully about how you are going to start. Plan just how you are going to use the time and resources at your disposal. Broadly speaking, all examination boards will mark your project under five headings:

- Identification of problem.
- Research and analysis.
- Selection and development.
- Realization or making.
- Evaluation.

Marks will be awarded under each section, so make sure you distribute your time evenly, bearing in mind the way marks are going to be apportioned.

Remember, all design problems have constraints — make sure you know yours at the outset! What facilities are available, can you obtain all the materials you will require, will you be able to complete in the time available? These and many other questions will need answering.

IDENTIFY A PROBLEM — I'VE GOT LOST THREE TIMES TRYING TO FIND YOUR SCHOOL MY FIRST IMPRESSIONS AREN'T GOOD!

RESEARCH AND ANALYSIS — WE TAKE IT FOR GRANTED BUT IF YOU'VE NOT BEEN HERE BEFORE...

SELECTION AND DEVELOPMENT — COULD YOU TRY THESE OUT AND GIVE ME YOUR COMMENTS

Stage 4

Spend time thinking carefully about how your project will be presented. More emphasis is placed on the presentation of your work in the design and communication part of craft, design and technology than in the other two areas. You are being examined on your ability to communicate solutions as well as how you find the solutions. Your final presentation will consist of a design folio, and mock-ups and models which illustrate your ideas in three dimensions. Your folio should have a sense of unity, a corporate style. Make decisions about the folio's appearance before you start. It too has to be designed. Think about size of paper, page layouts, index, and the organization of the various elements. Look at the two examples on this page. Which do you think communicates the story of the project well?

Remember that quality of presentation is very important. It will establish an examiner's first impression of your work.

Final word of advice

You may be very lucky — you may know exactly what you want to do for your project, easily find a problem which is within your scope and be raring to go. If so you are probably an exception!

If, on the other hand, you are finding it difficult then follow this procedure:

1 Select one of the four main categories covered in this unit (environmental, information, technological or industrial design).
2 Examine the possible project areas within the category and choose the area which most appeals to you.
3 Carry out a research project. For example, if you chose information design and then packaging you could follow the research project described on page 78. Most likely you will have to devise your own research project, but the examples given will show you how to approach it.

4 Once you have completed your research you will be something of an expert in your chosen area. It is most likely that by looking around and asking questions about what already exists, you will discover a wide range of possible projects. You will discover solutions that could be improved or solved differently, or needs which as yet have not been really satisfied or even identified.

Professional designers would give you this advice:

- Never design in a vacuum; gather as much information as you can before you start suggesting solutions.
- Don't re-invent the wheel; always have a look at how others have solved a problem before you start. They will probably have done a lot of the hard work for you!
- Design is about making improvements to what already exists. Don't confuse it with invention.
- Listen to what the client wants. Then try and interpret the requirements with a fresh pair of eyes, but don't lose sight of what the client said. Make sure you are both on the same road.

The remainder of this unit will illustrate a number of projects carried out by professional designers and students. There are four sections:

- Environmental design.
- Information design.
- Technological design.
- Industrial design.

In each section you will find three elements:

1 The story of a professional design project.
2 An example of a student's project consisting of a selection of the design sheets from the project.
3 A page of possible project areas — these are not provided for you to copy directly. As you know, marks are awarded for originating your own project brief. These briefs serve to illustrate the range of possible projects.

REALIZATION   EVALUATION

THANK YOU FOR YOUR TRAVELLING DIRECTIONS, I CAME STRAIGHT HERE, WHAT A WELL ORGANIZED SCHOOL.

Environmental design – student project

Once she had decided to undertake an architectural project, Barbara spent some time deciding exactly what to do. Eventually she settled on looking at the area of conversion. It has become a fairly fashionable trend in recent years to live in an old building – one which had out-served its usefulness but was too good to be demolished. There are examples all over the country of churches, schools, stations, warehouses etc. which have been given a new lease of life by being converted for residential use.

The first step for Barbara was to have a look at some examples. She looked at a range of rural buildings such as barns, and also at the multitude of conversions taking place in London's docklands. Her first choice as a project was to convert a disused water tower, but it proved difficult to gain access and the owners were not very co-operative. Finally she settled on the conversion of a barn. The architect commissioned by the owners to do the conversion was extremely helpful and explained how to set about the project – you can see the results of Barbara's work on these two pages.

Planning

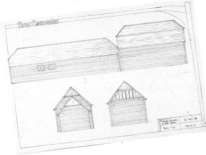
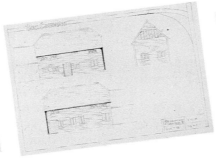
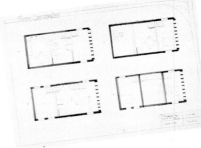

Construction

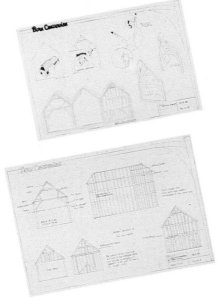

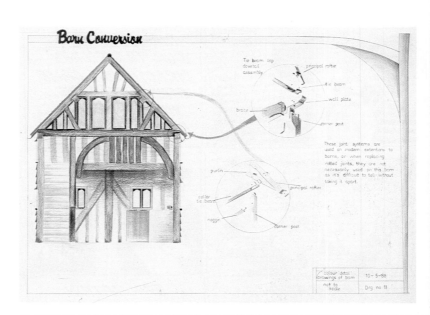

Presentation

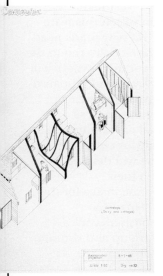

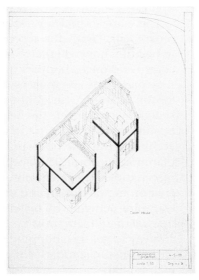

Realization

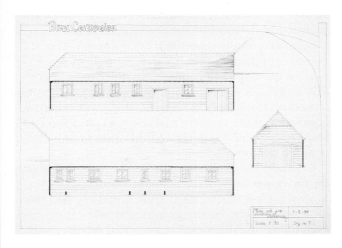

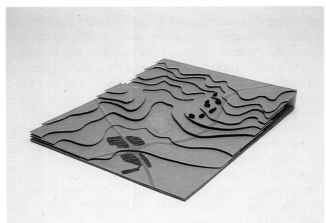

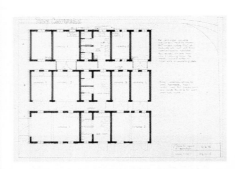

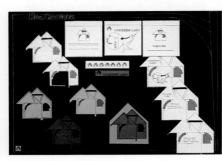

Crighton

Crighton is a relatively new design consultancy, established in 1984. The consultancy has grown rapidly and now has 65 employees, over two-thirds of whom are designers. Fifty per cent of Crighton's work relates to shopping centre design. This division is headed by Stephen Walsh, one of the consultancy's founding partners. Crighton is an international company and is involved in a number of design projects at any one time. In 1986 they started design work on a shopping centre in the heart of Liverpool — Clayton Square, close to Lime Street Station, a prime retailing location.

Shopping centres are the retail revolution of the 1980s. They have changed our expectations of and our attitudes to the way in which we shop. We might spend a day at a shopping centre and our every need would be catered for. Shopping centres show a change in the relationships between the three vital elements: the manufacturer, the retailer and the consumer. During the 1950s and 1960s the manufacturer dominated; goods were produced and it was the retailer's job to sell them. In the 1970s firms like Habitat and Marks & Spencer, the retailers, started to take control. They told their manufacturers what they wanted to sell. Now in the 1980s, it is the consumer who is the dominating force. At last it is a buyer's market, and both the manufacturer and the retailer are trying to satisfy the consumer's demands.

The story of any shopping centre starts with the developer — the client. In Liverpool, Wimpey Property acquired the land with the objective of developing Clayton Square shopping centre. They then appointed three other organizations: an architectural practice to be responsible for the fabric of the building; a design consultancy to be responsible for the interior, the image and eventually all the shoppers' needs; and the letting agents, the company responsible for selling space to retailers. These three organizations work together to meet their client's (the developer's) brief; the client will take their advice but has final control. The developers are responsible to their shareholders who will want to make a sound return on their investment.

There are several key issues on which this team must focus. Firstly the access — do new roads need to be built, how will merchandise be delivered to the centre and once shoppers have got there where will they park? The site must be surveyed and prepared for the builders. The architects must produce a scheme which meets the brief and is seen as a positive contribution to the visual environment. The architects will also be responsible for obtaining planning approval. The designers will develop a merchandising strategy on which their environmental design and corporate image for the shopping scheme will be based. Finally, a management team must be established, with a strategy to get the shopping centre up and running and to ensure standards of presentation are maintained.

Seymour Harris were appointed as architects for the scheme. Clayton Square will be a medium-sized shopping centre with a total floor area of about 24 000 m^2 (265 000 ft^2) of which 14 400 m^2 will be let to retailers. As you can see the architects have produced a totally controlled environment. The centre is on two levels with an atrium providing natural lighting in the concourse (the public space). The architects were responsible for all aspects of the structure, the supply of services, the environmental controls and the centre's maintenance. It is the responsibility of the design consultants to give the centre a personality or image.

Crighton were initially asked to be responsible only for the upper level of the scheme. Gradually, however, their involvement grew until they had the brief for creating the image for the whole centre, and then for selling the image to potential retailers and shoppers. It has been estimated that 80 per cent of the British population live within driving time of not one, but two shopping centres. If the shopper has a choice, then the total image of a centre becomes one of the crucial deciding factors about where to shop. At the outset of any project the target market or customer base has to be identified.

The initial thinking behind Clayton Square was that the lower level would be an extension of the surrounding streets, in particular Church Street. This area, the main body of the scheme, would be devoted to multiple retailers. The upper level was conceived as a haven of quality, something slightly different and distinctive. Research needed to be undertaken to identify the potential market. This normally takes the form of face-to-face interviews on the spot. The designers need to discover who shops in the area, what they are looking for, what they aspire to, what improvements they would like to see, and what spending power they have. If the market researchers provide the design team with an accurate profile of the likely customers, then there is a good chance that they will produce the most appropriate solution.

Caroline Cole was responsible for commissioning the research which revealed the target customer to be female, aged between 16 and 35. Shoppers come to this area from all over Liverpool for specialized shops, looking for personal and luxury goods, not for necessities. The survey revealed that these shoppers wanted more quality and variety, particularly in fashion wear. Average spending was in the region of £40 per trip for this type of shopper. The design team concluded, in consultation with the clients, that Clayton Square should be a centre devoted to fashion goods and that the design should complement and reinforce the notion of indulgent merchandise.

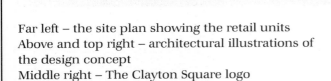

Far left – the site plan showing the retail units
Above and top right – architectural illustrations of the design concept
Middle right – The Clayton Square logo
Right – an early model of the development

The project now passed to Jon Wealleans, creative director at Crighton. The focus of attention was on the upper level: specialized shops selling quality goods not commonly found in shopping centres. A name for the area, the Gallery, was chosen to encourage shoppers to browse and look, to shop without specific objectives, to buy what takes their fancy, in a quiet relaxing environment. Conceptual drawings of the interior were produced. The image was refined until the design team felt that they were close to an answer. Elementary models were made and once these were approved a final, highly detailed model was commissioned. The model was used to finalize every aspect of the design and to sell the space to retailers.

The merchandising mix reflects a 'pampering the body' theme. Jon decided to make a feature of kiosk traders within the mall. Highly stylized kiosks were designed and modelled. The kiosks are let to traders selling goods which have pleasant aromas — flowers, perfumes, coffee, chocolate etc. This adds a further sensation to shopping in the Gallery. The notion that a trip to the Gallery will be a pleasure outing is enhanced by two specialized food courts offering culinary experiences which complement the image.

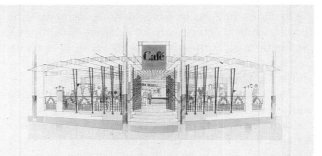

There is a great deal to the design team's role; they are responsible, for example, for the graphics of the information signs. These have been designed to complement the centre signs. The examples shown illustrate the designers' solution. Initially the colourway for the sign system was different, but it was changed after discussion with the client.

Above — design sheets of the interior of Claytor Square

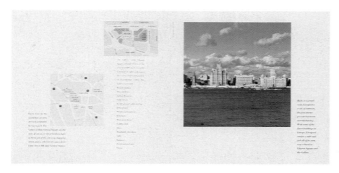

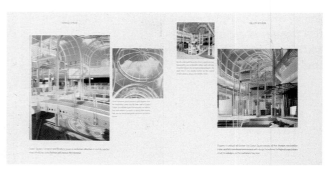

All the organizations in the developer's team worked to a month-by-month programme designed to ensure that the centre opened in time for Christmas trading, 1988.

Crighton's marketing manager Sarah Coles is responsible for marketing the centre. It is her task to keep everyone informed about the centre's development — the media, the local chamber of commerce, potential retailers, pressure groups and the eventual shoppers.

This openness has been essential with this development, as Georgian buildings were demolished to make way for Clayton Square and this aroused strong local feelings. The site hoardings have been used to display information and give progress reports. A small exhibition area has given the public the chance to view the model. Crighton is also responsible for producing the brochure aimed at selling the retail space. This must convince potential retailers that it will be a profitable location, a shopping centre which has a clear identity and will attract their type of customer. As you can see, the role of the design consultancy is all embracing. Crighton employ a wide range of professional skills so that every aspect of the design brief can be met. Their task is to design through the consumer's eye, to provide an environment which will make spending a pleasure.

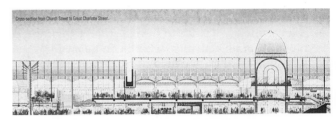

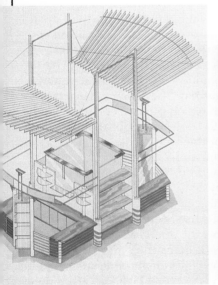

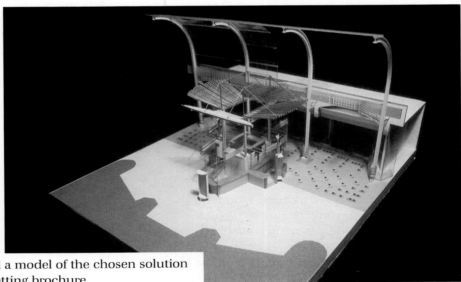

Above — design of the kiosk and a model of the chosen solution
Below — pages from the retail letting brochure

Architecture Set Design for T.V. & Theatre **Exhibition Design Interior Design** *Town Planning* Shop Window Design

Typical project briefs

- Make a study of waiting rooms, at the dentist's or the doctor's. Analyse the needs of such areas from the point of view of those using them. From the waiting rooms which you visit, select one and redesign it in an attempt to improve it for those who use it. Present your redesign in the most appropriate way to communicate your ideas to the potential client.

    This project could be modified to include any variety of functional interior such as reception areas or offices.

- A local society wishes to have a small exhibition illustrating its activities, which can be easily transported and quickly mounted in venues such as public libraries. You have been asked to design the exhibition system. Your final solution should be in the form of a model which will demonstrate how the exhibition will be erected.

- The landscape around the entrance to your school needs to be improved. The PTA is willing to pay for the cost of the materials and to provide help with the landscaping and small-scale building which might be required. You have decided to enter the competition to find the best design. The competition rules require a site model of the finished design for the final judging.

- Design a self-catering holiday chalet to sleep six people. The chalet will be one of 30 in a holiday village. It must be designed in sympathy with the local environment. You may select the specific location — it can be anywhere. Produce a brochure which could be sent to possible clients giving them all the information about the chalet which they would require.

- Make a study of three housing estates, paying particular attention to the spatial arrangement of the houses. Produce analytical drawings of each estate in relation to the following aspects: safety, privacy and public space. On the basis of your research select one estate and attempt to redesign its layout to improve it for its inhabitants.

- A large store requires a shop window display to feature one of its departments. Select an appropriate shop and window, decide on the department and design a display.

    Alternatively, the display could be seasonal such as for Christmas, or thematic such as for 5 November.

- Make a study of your city or town centre from the point of view of the disabled. Consider how easy it is for them to get around and find the things they want. Prepare a set of recommendations which, if implemented, would make it much easier for them. Remember that if someone has a disability, they often compensate by developing one of their other senses, for example the blind have a highly developed tactile sensitivity.

- Explore your local surroundings and find a building which looks run down, ready for redeveloping and for a new role. It may be a farm building such as a barn, an empty village school, a disused industrial building or something similar. Make proposals of how the building might be converted into residential accommodation. The detail of your proposal will depend on the scale of the building. If it is large, you will be most concerned with how the building is divided up. If it is large enough for only one house, you will be able to make more detailed plans and models.

- A housing estate is just being completed. As part of their selling promotion, the builders are offering to landscape the garden. They wish to have three show gardens from which purchasers can select. The gardens should be designed for the following three types: one for the keen gardener, a low maintenance garden and a garden for a family with two young children. The plots are all the same size — 8 m by 20 m. Design and model the three show gardens.

- A double-decker bus has been purchased by a local community organization as a pre-school play bus. The inside needs converting into a suitable environment for the children and their helpers. Produce a solution which will take into account all their needs. You should also consider the exterior of the bus.

- Design and model a stage set for one of the plays which you are studying or have studied in English.

- Theme parks and museums are one of the current boom sectors in the leisure industry. Find out as much as you can about the ones currently open, such as Alton Towers and Disneyland, and those currently being developed, such as the Battersea Power Station conversion and Wonder World at Corby. From your research plan your own imaginary theme park or design in more detail one possible attraction.

Corporate Identity Packaging Sign Design Information Graphics Illustration Typography

Typical project briefs

- A publishing house is bringing out a new series of 'Teach Yourself' guides aimed at the proposed national curriculum for secondary school pupils. They require a name for the series and cover designs for each of the volumes. Design the total package, including any other items which you think are necessary.

- The tourist authority of your local town or village requires a new information leaflet about what to see for visitors and tourists. They have decided that it should be in the form of an illustrated walkers' guide. As they wish to give it away free, it must consist of a single A4 sheet which is printed on both sides. After investigating the locality and deciding on what should be included, design the leaflet and produce a finished version for evaluation.

- A company has decided to promote its product by commissioning you to design a direct mail advertisement to be sent to potential customers. They envisage that it will be dynamic, e.g. pop-up or constructional. The finished design should feature the company's product and be attractive so that the recipient will wish to keep it rather than throwing it away.

  You can select your own company. It could be an hotel, an estate agent, a manufacturer of graphics materials, a car hire firm, a furniture retailer — the choice is limitless.

- Select a local tourist attraction and design a new sign system. You should not only design the signs, but also investigate their positioning. Possible tourist attractions are castles, stately homes, parks and nature reserves, zoos, and museums.

- Your school has been asked to mount an exhibition in the Town Hall to illustrate the life and work of the school. It will consist of a number of panels, each focusing on particular aspects of the life of the school. The display area on each panel measures 800 mm × 1400 mm. Select one of the following areas and design and produce the finished panel: clubs and societies, examination system or the school's resources.

- A national charity is to send a desk-top calendar to all its regular contributors. The calendar is to be made out of card and must fit into an A5 envelope. Design and make a possible solution.

  You should select your own charity.

  Alternatively, you could substitute a lay-flat card collecting box instead of the calendar.

- Design, manufacture and evaluate a board game. Your final prototype should include rules and everything required to play the game, and be packaged ready for point-of-sale display.

- Select a product which does a job, such as a power drill, food mixer or something similar. Design and produce a booklet which explains how it should be used.

- The government often designates each year to a particular cause. They have decided to have a Year of the Countryside. The aim will be to encourage everyone to be more concerned about preserving the countryside and to make it more accessible. A logo needs to be designed and an advertising campaign devised to get the message across. Produce a dossier to illustrate how you would implement such a campaign, given the opportunity.

  You could change the focus of the year to any cause which you feel needs promoting in this way.

- Packaging is designed to achieve a number of objectives such as ensuring the product is safely transported, promoting the image of the product and giving information about the product. Select a good and bad example of each case and, using annotated visuals, justify your selection. In the light of what you have learnt, carry out a repackaging exercise on one of the examples you selected as being poor.

- A leading manufacturer of detergents is launching a new cold wash automatic soap powder. The powder needs a name and package. The manufacturer wants the powder to have a hi-tech image — state of the art washing. Produce all the elements you would require to make a product presentation to the client.

- A small local company wishes to completely redesign its corporate identity — everything from letterheads to logo. Your task is to produce a proposal which shows clearly how your design will be implemented.

- A travel company wishes to supply clients with a travel kit when they purchase a holiday through them. The kit should contain the obvious items such as baggage labels, but also other items that a traveller might require. The kit should be packaged in card in the house style of the company. Select a company and design and make a solution to this brief.

Information design — student project

Gary was interested in undertaking a project for an actual client, someone who would be critical of his work in a realistic and honest fashion. As his other major interests were sporting, Gary wanted to have a go at a graphics project with a sporting flavour. After a number of ideas had been considered, he hit on the idea of undertaking a corporate identity program for a sports shop. This seemed like a good idea, providing he could find a sports shop.

It did not take too long to discover a local sports shop that was willing to act as a client for Gary's project, with the promise that if they liked the results they would consider using his designs. The first task was to design the logo. This developed in consultation with the client. Once agreement on the logo was reached, Gary set about implementing the design. He produced letterheads, business cards, tee shirts and van paint schemes. You can see from these two pages just how thorough he was.

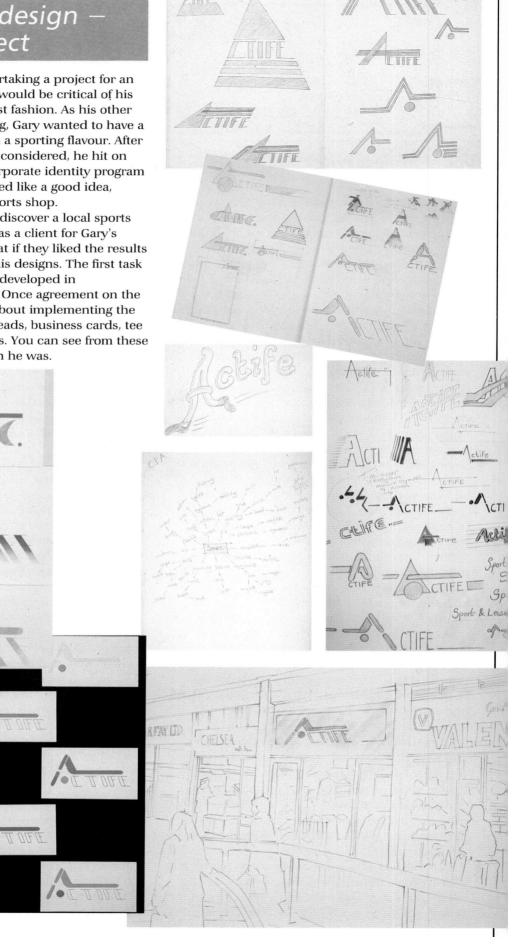

Nettle

The way designers work depends on their particular field of expertise. The architect may be involved with a design project for several years. This is also true of the car designer. However, computers are shortening the time scale of many of these projects. At the other end of the scale, the designer faced with a packaging project for a large supermarket or chain of retail outlets might have to find the right solution to the client's needs in as short a period as five weeks.

Packaging usually falls within the province of the graphic designer. A graphic design consultancy might also tackle corporate design briefs, exhibition design, brochure and leaflet projects and point-of-sale displays, amongst many other things. Consultancies vary in size. Large ones will carry out every aspect of a project in-house. This will mean employing photographers and illustrators as well as all the other specialized services which are necessary to the design process. A smaller consultancy will farm work out to firms or freelance individuals who offer a particular service.

Nettle Design is a consultancy which specializes in packaging design. It is a fairly small yet highly successful consultancy whose work is on display, and can be viewed free of charge in the high street, and yet like much of any designer's work is nameless. Packaging is an art form. It is the manufacturer's final ploy to seduce the consumer into buying their product and not that of a rival. Often it appears that more thought goes into the packaging than the product! Nettle has eight employees, four of whom are designers. John Hurst looks after the business side of the consultancy whilst Glyn West is the creative director. Both had worked for other designers before going it alone.

Right — the UHU packaging as it was prior to being redesigned

The consultancy was established in 1978, and in 1983 they moved to their present studio. They occupy the fifth floor of a converted warehouse at Wapping, in the heart of London's dockland. Metropolitan Wharf was one of the first docklands to be converted. It was divided into small units, ideal for workshops and studios. The designer's imagination and vision showed how disused buildings could be converted for new uses. There are now many examples of conversions which have resulted in new life being breathed into areas of decay.

Nettle's list of clients is impressive; Boots, Dairy Crest, United Biscuits, Beecham, Lyons Maid, House of Fraser and Asda have all benefited from their design skills. One of their most important clients is Beecham Toiletries and Healthcare, a division of the international conglomerate Beecham Group, based at Brentford, West London. Just imagine the amount of creative packaging there is on display in any shopping centre or hypermarket. There are the large companies such as Heinz, Kelloggs, and Crosse and Blackwell. Then there are the brand names: Marmite, Ajax, Shape, for example. All these have images and messages which must be conveyed through the packaging. A company as large as Beecham will sell products under its own name, but will also sell products under brand names. It was with one of these branded products, UHU, which Nettle become involved.

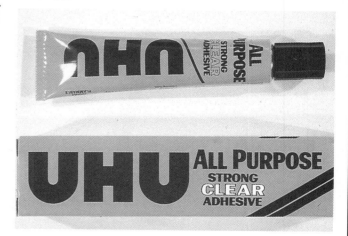

Nettle has worked on a number of products for Beecham. The client is Rosemary Cooke, one of the company's marketing managers. Rosemary controls a team of product managers and assistant product managers. One of the products for which she is responsible is UHU glue. It is a household name, an all-purpose glue which comes in a tube and can be used to glue 'virtually anything — UHU dries fast and holds fast, a must for every household, office and school'. The glue has a strong product identity, recognizable by its packaging — striking yellow and black colours. Rosemary felt that although the brand had been successful over the years, the competition was hotting up. This is one of the responsibilities of any marketing division: keeping a close eye on the competition. New products, repackaging and increased promotion appear — Rosemary must be aware of the competition's sales drive and react accordingly to ensure the market niche of the products for which she is responsible. It was also felt that the packaging had become slightly dated. All factors pointed to a repackaging and relaunch, and with it the opportunity to improve the level of communication on the pack — the product's uses clearly stated with simple, easy-to-follow instructions. Rosemary's next step was to select a consultancy which could handle the job successfully and at a competitive price!

Initial ideas for the new packaging

Once a product manager decides that a range of products requires repackaging or a new range is to be introduced, the design process moves rapidly into action. Rosmary's first action is to ask consultancies to tender for the job. The brief would be sent to consultancies that may have previously worked for Beecham, or consultancies whose work she feels is in sympathy with the image she envisages for the product. Consultancies need to advertise their work

through specialized journals to bring it to the attention of product managers. For the UHU job Rosemary contacted two consultancies. Nettle were asked to submit examples of their work to prove they had the experience to cope with package graphics which would include a high content of information. They also had to give an estimate of what it would cost. This sometimes takes place at a presentation to the client. The professional jargon for this is making a pitch!

The first Nettle will know of their selection is when the fax machine starts to generate the brief. Once the consultancy is alerted it must work quickly. John Hurst produces a quotation. It must include every aspect of the job. Once it is agreed there can be no changes — the work must be completed within budget. Nettle's competitive bid and expertise won them the contract. Given the go-ahead Glyn West, the creative director, can start work on initial concepts. As many as five will be produced within about eighteen days. These are generally in the form of flat colour roughs. They will be discussed with Rosemary and the most suitable concept selected. The selected concept will then be developed into a completed solution. The time scale is in the region of seven to eight days.

The glue had previously been packed in a variety of ways such as card boxes, but most recently it has been sold in blister packs. Such packs are easy to display, give good visibility to the product and provide space for information — good reasons to retain that type of pack. The product range also includes glue sticks and aerosol cans. Nettle had to develop a consistent image suitable for each product. It was also important that a link was maintained between the existing identity and the new one. For this reason it was decided to retain the distinctive colours. The brand image needs to be as strong as possible to make the product highly visible at the point-of-sale display, especially as research has revealed that the product is often an impulse purchase, bought just in case something gets broken, useful to have around. An important aspect of the

new packaging is to tell the customer, and user, the various uses of each product. Many people are confused when selecting the right adhesive for a particular task. If they buy the wrong one they will probably buy a competitor's product next time.

Some companies submit proposals to a packaging review committee. This might be a sample of company employees representing every aspect of the organization, or it might include members of the general public. The product manager will present the packs explaining the thinking behind the concept and solution. A committee has three options: it will either accept without reservation; approve but with some suggestions as to changes which they believe will improve the design; or they can reject the solution and ask the product manager to start afresh with a new consultancy. In other companies, the decision might be taken by senior management. However a decision is reached, it will not be taken by one individual.

The chosen design is a visual development from the old one. A sense of continuity has been maintained. The background is still predominantly yellow and line illustrations have been introduced on to the packs to explain the uses of each product. In addition, a red border has been introduced around each blister to further highlight the product. You can judge for yourself whether the solution is successful.

Once Nettle had received approval for their designs they could set about producing the finished artwork to be sent to the printers. Their final task is to check proofs, both text and printing accuracy, including correct colours and quality. The whole process took seven weeks from start to finish. Few other branches of the design world work at such speed, yet still have to distil fresh, imaginative solutions from the client's brief — no time to wait for inspiration, it has to be worked out at the end of a pencil!

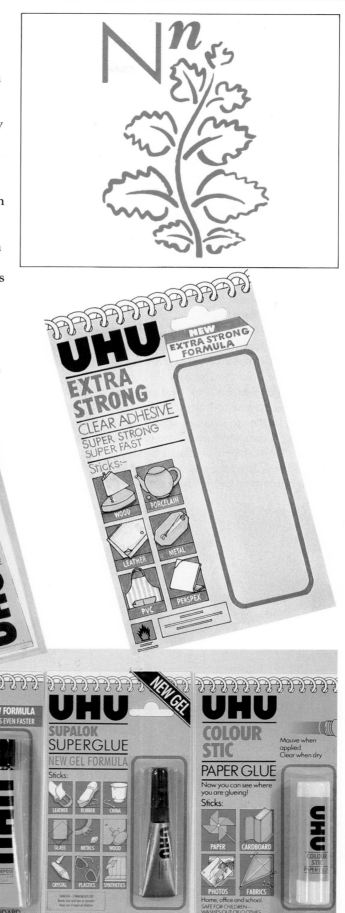

The chosen solution developed as far as a prototype model

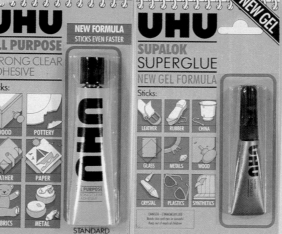

Technological design – student project

Gillian was extremely interested in environmental issues, in particular alternative technology. Living in Cumbria she was extremely concerned about the use of nuclear power and the long-term effects which it might have on the environment. Initially she carried out a great deal of research into energy sources, the finite life of fuel supplies and the possible alternatives. At this point she did not quite know which way to proceed. The first idea was to produce a computer game based on the use of energy which would be fun but at the same time informative. However, this, after considering what was involved, seemed far too ambitious.

Above all Gillian wanted to produce something that would educate people. She felt that in general people knew far too little about the issues involved. Finally she decided to put all her research to good use and produce a pop-up book on energy. It would present the information in an interesting and dynamic way, something that people would want to learn from, in particular young people who might have the power to change or influence policy in the future. You can see how some of the pages were designed and developed into working prototypes. The end result was a real tour de force and achieved all the objectives Gillian had set herself.

Page 1 - 2 — WARM COLOUR RANGE

— VERTICAL AXIS FORMAT - Because it allows for more . hinging space to construct pop up model between i.e

Full length of axis could fit 2 pop up onto one hinge

. First page devoted to the history of energy — DIAL BASED
2nd page → types of energy represented by the car. BOTH pages do not require a form to be fixed across the hinge - eg
History - flat Dial form . Car - sliding and fold on/off leaves superimposed

Therefore page 1 - 2 are compatable.

PAGE ①

A — POSITIONED AT THE TOP WINDOW

- YELLOW
- INNER - BACK G
- RED - BROWN HIGHLIGHTS

- YELLOW OUTER
- PINK INNER
- RED BORDER

→ Explain content. new Dial positions

12 SECTIONS

→ THUMB CUT OUT

→ CONCLUSION — SUM UP

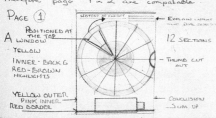

Double glazing
Draft exclusion doors
- More light let in windows

Lights over work places
- Toilet waste methane gen

HEAT PUMP

Radiators not under window

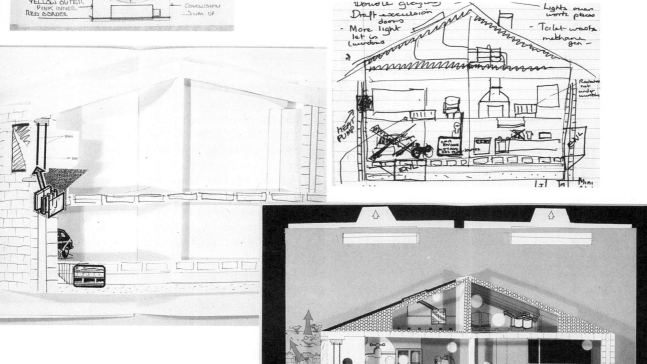

Keraflo Ltd

The task of the engineering designer is to improve the quality of people's lives. It may involve the design and development of glamorous projects such as bridges, cars and aircraft, or hi-tech equipment, for example life saving medical equipment or advanced communication systems. These products are often in the news. The engineer is also responsible for many things which we take for granted, like the supply of essential services: gas, water and electricity. Engineers are specialists in particular fields, for example civil, electrical, electronic and aeronautic engineering. This case study tells the story of the design, development and production of a mechanical engineering project.

Engineers are always seeking to improve on existing designs: make them more efficient, longer lasting, easier to service, cheaper to produce and so on. Some products or principles last the test of time and become firmly established. It then takes a person with vision to rethink radically such a product. Maurice Thompson was an engineer and consultant in the water supply and plumbing industry. He believed that the ball and equilibrium valve fitted in WC cisterns and storage tanks could be redesigned and improved in a number of ways. This is certainly not a glamour product, but one which we take for granted until the washer goes or the ballcock sticks. He believed it was possible to design a maintenance-free valve which would be both quieter and quicker.

Before you read any further it would be a good idea to go and take the lid off the WC cistern and see how it operates. You will probably see either a copper or a coloured plastic ball on the end of an arm which is connected to a valve. This controls the water supply into the cistern. Flush the toilet and the ball will fall as the water level drops, opening the valve so that the cistern starts to refill. It appears to be pretty efficient, so why bother to redesign the valve? The truth is, it is not! Eight million valves are replaced annually, 80 per cent of all sales. Local authorities replace 1.5 million valves a year and that costs them at least £30 million including labour. New water bylaws also require a drop in cistern capacity from 9 to 7 litres, and as a result, valves will have to be more compact.

Maurice believed he had the answer. The washers in water taps are gradually being replaced by ceramic discs. They have many advantages. The tap can be operated by a small angular movement, it is maintenance free and never leaks in the closed position. Apply this new technology to the water cistern valve and it too would be improved as dramatically. It sounds straightforward but it took a three-year period of development to make the idea a reality.

Maurice had the idea but he needed a backer, someone who would fund the research. Eventually

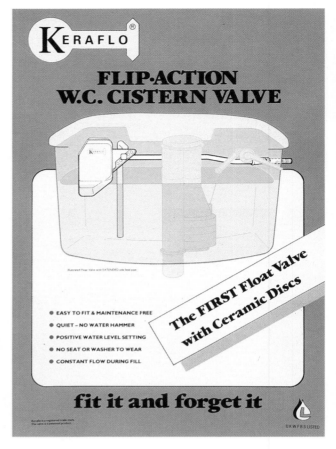

he teamed up with Lawrence Burns, a high-tech entrepreneur, who believed that Maurice's idea was a potential winner, and together they formed Keraflo Ltd. A decision had to be taken: should the company take out a patent and then sell companies a licence to manufacture; or team up with a larger company; or go it alone? They opted to go it alone as they believed that this would be the simplest and quickest way to success. The next step was to employ a design development engineer to oversee the production of a prototype and to set up a manufacturing operation. Peter Clark joined the team and an operating base was established.

You can see Maurice's original sketches from which Peter worked. The valve consists of two ceramic discs, in permanent contact. A rotation of 60 degrees opens and closes the valve. The discs, almost as hard as diamonds, are polished to a tolerance of 0.0005 mm, so smooth that in contact they form a perfect seal. This can also cause problems. Highly polished discs grow together if the surfaces are not permanently greased. This is achieved by creating a porous surface to the disc and charging these pores with grease. Peter needed to carry out a great deal of research to solve this problem. His eventual answer is highly innovative. The discs are spring-loaded to ensure permanent surface contact, and the surface contact is kept to a minimum to prevent sticking. The assembled sectioned view of the valve shows the final design. All components are injection moulded in acetal which is a tough polymer, having a high resistance to water absorption.

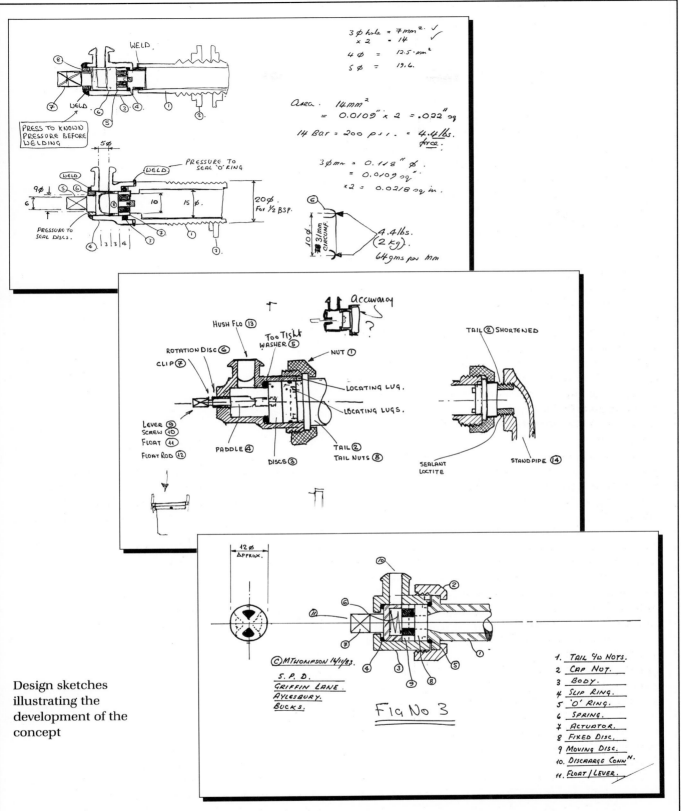

Design sketches
illustrating the
development of the
concept

The team now turned its attention to the rest of the system. The float needed to be made more compact to fit smaller cisterns. In addition, fast fill and cut-off would make the system more efficient. The traditional ballcock gradually closes the valve as the cistern fills. If the valve could open instantly and stay fully open until the correct level had been reached, a quicker fill would be achieved. To do this Peter did a great deal of calculation relating to the form of the float. The solution has created a unique flip action: on/off water control. The shape of the float acts to keep the valve open until the correct level has been reached. Then the centre of buoyancy moves instantly away from the middle and the float flips up closing the valve. The same principle is employed by marine architects when designing self-righting lifeboats. It is known as metrocentric buoyancy.

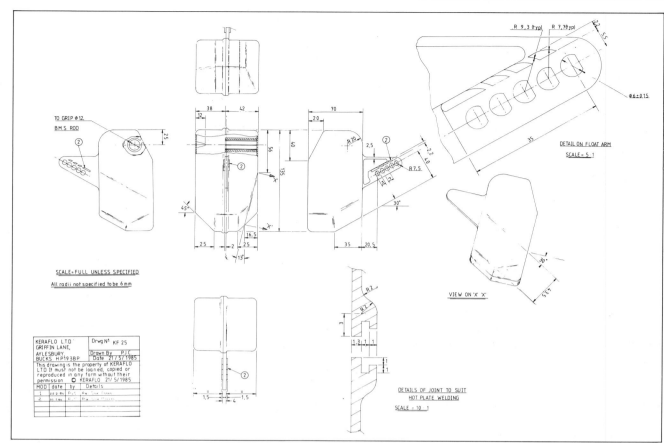

The float is moulded in two halves in polypropylene. A weight is inserted to ensure that the valve opens, then the two halves are welded together on a hot plate. The design compensates for the fact that as the float pops up, the water level will fall. It is also adjustable for different levels. It was decided to tackle the noise problem and produce a quieter fill. Peter knew the answer — a delivery tube to the base of the cistern. However, this solution infringed water regulations. If the water pressure suddenly drops it is possible for a vacuum to be created. If this occurred, water in the cistern would be sucked back into the general supply system. As bleach and other proprietary cleaners are often added to cisterns this might prove dangerous. This is not acceptable so the discharge director must be above the level of the water.

Another clever solution was called for. The answer was a tubular mesh from the discharge director to the bottom of the cistern. The mesh creates an aerated curtain which muffles the noise and acts as a silencer without allowing suck-back. Now Peter had to design a range of feed pipes so that the unit could be fitted to all existing cisterns. Three varieties are needed: a short (compact), long (extended), or bottom feed pipe. Moulded in acetal, their shapes were designed to prevent water hammer and make the cistern quieter. The valve must operate satisfactorily in both high- and low-pressure situations (normally 3 to 150 psi). In high-pressure situations the flow must be restricted to prevent continuous syphoning. The solution to this is a spiral in the feed pipe. This simply causes the water to flow further, round and round the spiral, slowing it down as a result of friction.

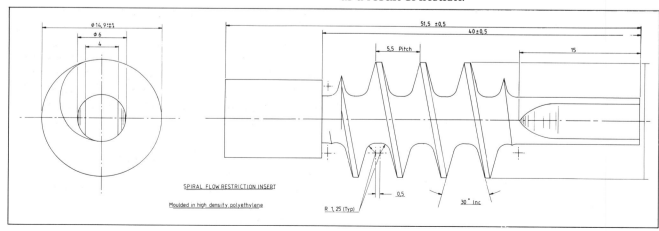

SPIRAL FLOW RESTRICTION INSERT

Moulded in high density polyethylene

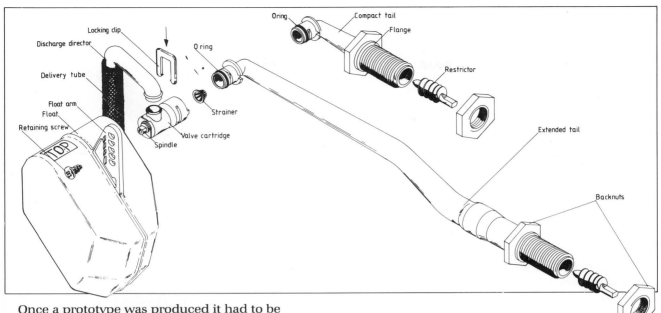

Locking clip · Discharge director · Delivery tube · Float arm · Float · Retaining screw · Spindle · Valve cartridge · Strainer · O ring · Oring · Compact tail · Flange · Restrictor · Extended tail · Backnuts · TOP

Once a prototype was produced it had to be tested. A test bed was built and exhaustive trials were carried out to prove reliability. The system had to be submitted to the Water Research Council (UK WFBS) for approval. Without their certificate, which guarantees compliance with water bylaws, it would not be accepted by the industry and the water authorities. This can take time and modifications might be required but, once approved, the Board's water drop kite mark of acceptance can be used on promotional literature.

Initially the valve was produced at a loss — this is true of all new products. As production built up to 10 000 units a month the cost of the research and development started to be recouped. The Keraflo valve is still more expensive than conventional valves so the initial sales drive is to the quality sector of the market. With the start of quantity production and assembly being carried out by unskilled labour the tolerance zones were quickly reduced. A higher level of automation demands levels of precision which cannot be achieved without significant capital investment. A classic dilemma: the company believes the price of the unit could be slashed if real mass-production could be achieved, but this involves financial risk. It may be the best valve on the market but that is not the end of the story. Real success will depend on the marketing operation.

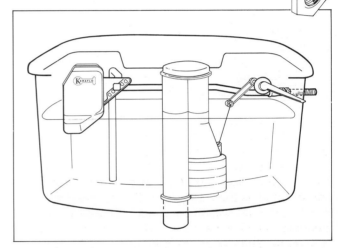

The designers required a range of communication skills; sketches to establish ideas; orthographic drawings of individual parts for mould makers; assembled sectional views to show the relationships of the parts and exploded views for the eventual installer, a plumber or DIY expert. The design engineers had a concept but they had to work methodically through a range of problems to reach a solution. Research, investigation, experimentation and intuition all played their part. The valve is suitable for a wide range of applications in a variety of storage situations. Design and development of a new product is always a gamble requiring both luck and faith. Some of you may even have seen one of these units when you examined your water cistern. Keraflo hope so, and who knows, in the future their valve may become the accepted standard, until another engineer comes up with a novel idea!

Top — an extended view of the valve
Top right — the float
Far left — the spiral which prevents continuous syphoning
Left — the valve cartridge

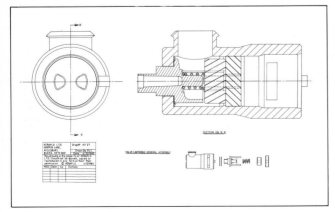

Industrial design – student project

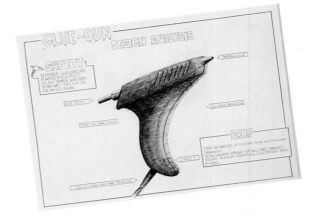

Bill had been using a glue gun to do some woodwork, and he had discovered how unsatisfactory the design was. The most annoying aspect was the lack of a stand, but he also found it uncomfortable to hold. This is the ideal situation to be in when it comes to selecting a project. If you actually come across something which is poorly designed and you think you can improve it, then why not have a go!

The first thing Bill did was to carry out some market research to see what else was on the market, and whether they all shared the same faults as the glue gun he had used. He then started to try out his ideas. His design developed until he reached a stage where he thought it was worth doing a presentation drawing. This confirmed his solution and he set about making a form model. He chose to make it out of jelutong so that he could obtain the precision he required. The surface finish was important and Bill spent a lot of time trying to reproduce the finish of an actual moulding. In the end he succeeded. An elegant design, it certainly solves the problems which Bill first encountered.

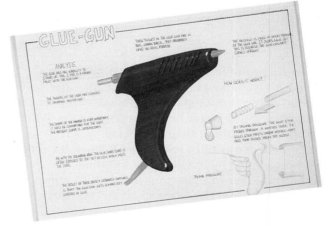

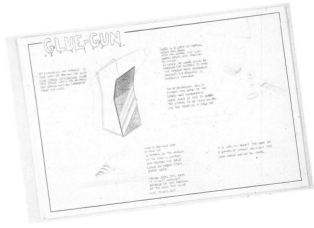

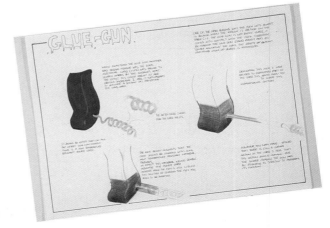

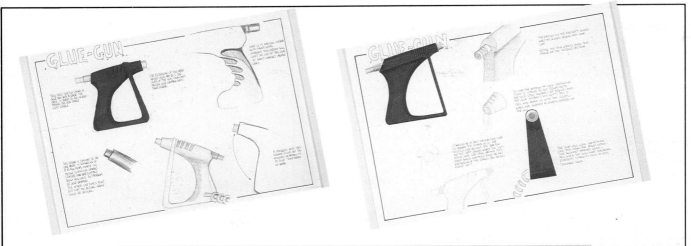

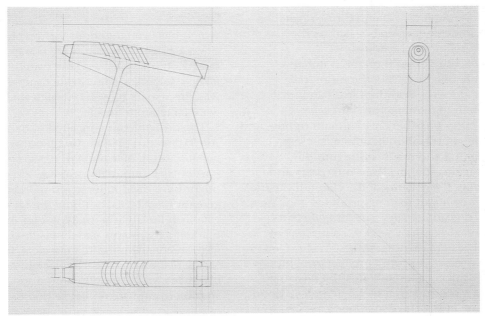

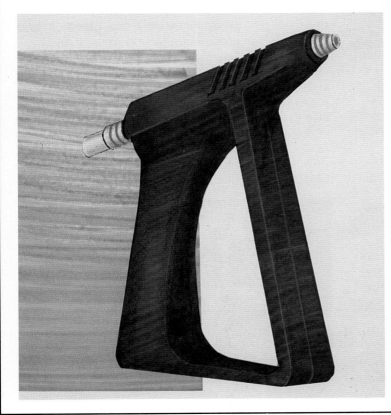

Roberts Weaver

Industrial designers tend to concentrate on the relationship between products and the people who use them. Their speciality is products that look good, are desirable and saleable, and are satisfying to own and use. They may have to tackle projects that vary in both scale and scope. Roberts Weaver are one of Britain's premier design consultancies with an international reputation. They design a wide range of products, from the interior of British Telecom International satellite tracking station at Goonhilly Down, to a set of domestic saucepans and hi-fi equipment. The project featured here is one undertaken for a Japanese client, Citizen Watches, who wanted some conceptual design work undertaken in relation to watches.

Philip Gray is the design director at Roberts Weaver. He believes the task of the industrial designer is to 'develop a product from an initial concept through to manufacture and sale, investigating every possible development option, and integrating the contribution of others, such as finance, marketing and engineering into the development team'. The designer interprets and turns into reality the dreams of the client. Industrial design is not just about making products 'look nice', it is far more. It is about their safe and efficient use, their reliability and ease of service, sound use of materials and ease of manufacture – in short, every aspect of the project. A product reflects a company's image and technical capability. It is the designer's task to design a product that looks right, feels good and catches the eye of the consumer.

Roberts Weaver was founded by Jos Roberts and Barrie Weaver in 1977. The consultancy has 52 employees of which 23 are qualified designers. Rapid expansion has taken place in the past few years and they now occupy converted buildings in a mews in west London. Linked to the design studios is RW Models Ltd. They undertake all the consultancy's model making requirements, but in addition also accept commissions from architects and the media for special effects. They also have a number of associate design organizations in other countries, notably one in Tokyo, Japan, and it is through this office that the work on the watch originated.

New technology has, in recent years, completely changed our attitude to watches and devices that tell the time. At the turn of the century watches were highly valued possessions, something to save up for and treasure. Watches were the pinnacle of miniaturized mechanical engineering. Yet now they might be given away as promotional gifts, or they can be purchased for a couple of pounds in a service station or street kiosk. The irony is that these cheap watches are more accurate timekeepers, have a bewildering number of functions and never need winding! You probably have a watch and take all these features for granted. It is of course quartz

which has brought about this revolution. As well as ensuring that watches are cheap and accurate, the quartz chip has allowed the watch to become a fashion accessory, not just a functional possession. It was this aspect of watch design that Roberts Weaver were called in to tackle.

The design team consisted of Barrie Weaver and Jon Tremlett. Their starting point was a consideration of life-styles, designing a watch for a particular group of consumers. Previously a company might have divided its world markets on a geographical basis, but now the tendency is to establish life-style stereotypes: for example, a sports market; a high-tech, gadget-fascinated group; the fashion conscious; and a classical, traditional, sophisticated market. The designers tried to establish life-style groups and illustrated the look they were seeking to capture on image boards. These consist of cuttings from magazines illustrating the kind of world each of these life-styles inhabits, the clothes they wear, the products they buy, the cars they drive, their choice of entertainment, and so on. Image boards give designers a feel for the market, the shapes and colours which are currently popular, the style and image which identifies this group – a visual context in which to design. These boards are also used to discuss with the clients their perception of the market they are trying to reach. The boards act as discussion prompts, they help ensure that both the client and the design team are in sympathy at the outset of the project.

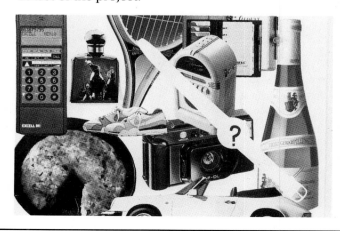

Now the designers could start in earnest. Concept sketches were produced by the dozen; several pages showing different styles and images. Each sketch was carefully crafted to illustrate the precise detail envisaged by the designer. In an object such as a watch the detailing is paramount. Subtle changes of angle, shape and colour can greatly alter the proportions and visual totality of the design. At this stage all preconceptions of analogue watch faces have been swept away, as you can see from the design sheet, one of many. Gradually a shape and image began to develop and evolve, as you can see in the next design sheet. The designers have chosen to use coloured pencils. The precision and subtlety they offer when working to this degree of accuracy on a small scale cannot be bettered. These are simple orthographic views, yet they present a total picture of the watch.

The selected idea now has to be developed. Exact proportions must be defined, and detailing must still be explored by making slight changes and assessing the results. You can see how the designer is using sketches to explore the shape of the display and the position of the buttons. At this stage the designer is using larger drawings as the degree of precision he requires is higher. Markers have been used to add form and colour. At the same time as developing the watch, the strap has been investigated. A watch strap has obvious functional aspects, to which there are a wide range of solutions, but it also has a visual and tactile quality which is of great importance. New materials such as high-grade, tear-proof polyurethane have changed the way in which the watch is held on the wrist and now there are also watches which are designed to be worn anywhere but on the wrist.

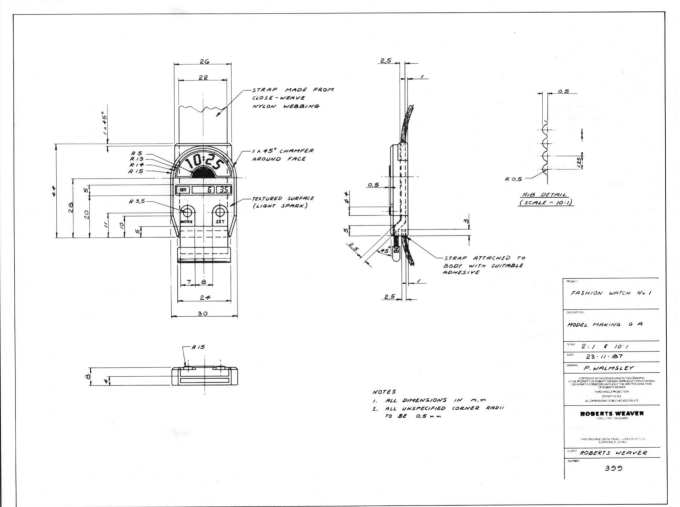

Above – a general arrangement of the final solution
Left – an image board

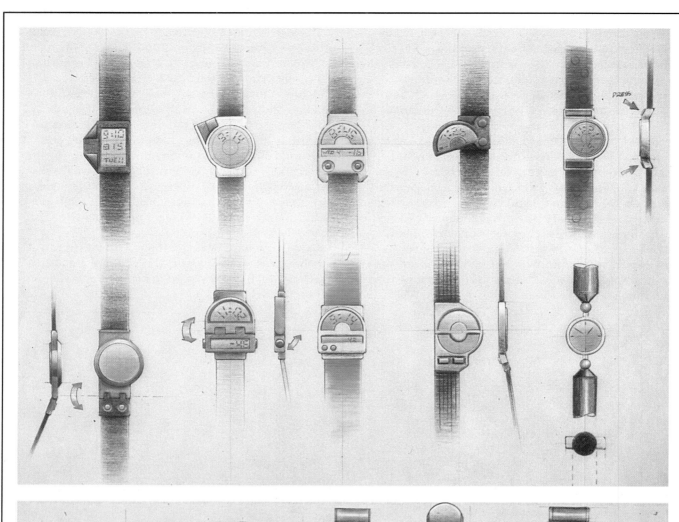

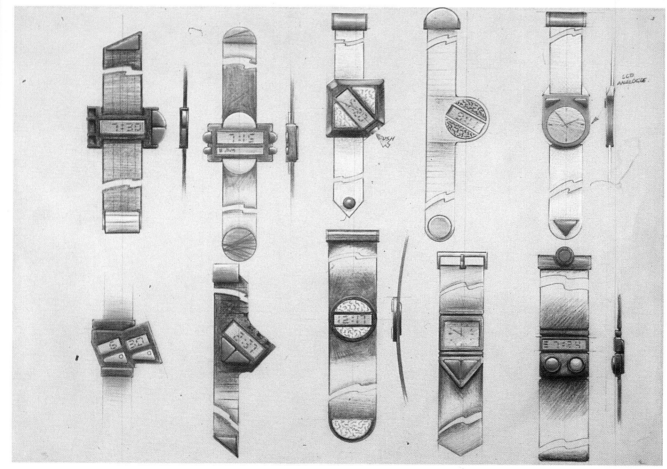

The concept must now be accurately modelled. This was undertaken by Ian McWilliams, the managing director of RW Models. A form model was made, precise in every detail, but with no movement. It always tells the same time — 10.25 a.m. The model is made life-size. It would have been easy to scale the model up, but if this had been done product photographs would have to have been shot out of context. This model can now be used to sell the design to the client. A photographic show would be used showing the model in its life-style setting — the sports market.

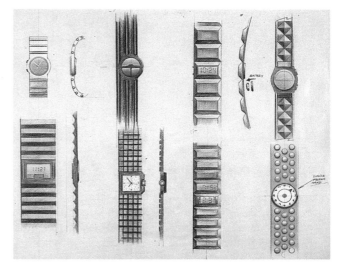

Barry Weaver's next step was to get the go-ahead from the client. This meant a mid-week trip to Japan. The final models were presented to Citizen. It is their task to decide on the method of manufacture, based on the design proposals. First the quartz movement, all the additional parts of the mechanism and the digital read-out must be fitted into the casing. Barry and Jon have been designing the packaging to house all these components. Next detailed drawings of the casing are prepared to ensure that the manufacturing department understands precisely the shape and finish required. Each part must be drawn individually in orthographic projection, and in addition there must be a general arrangement drawing showing the relationship of all the individual parts. These drawings finalize every aspect of the product — the design is complete. When tooling and production machinery has been completed the final task for the design team is to check the quality of production components to ensure the specifications have been met. Maybe some of Jon and Barry's other designs which were also taken to the model stage, and are shown at the foot of this page, will eventually find their way into our shops.

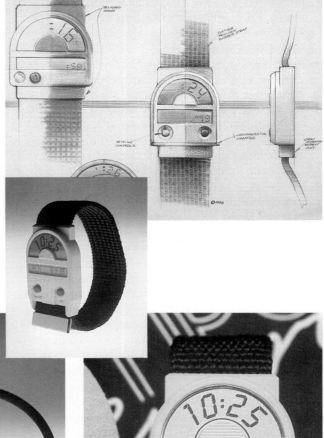

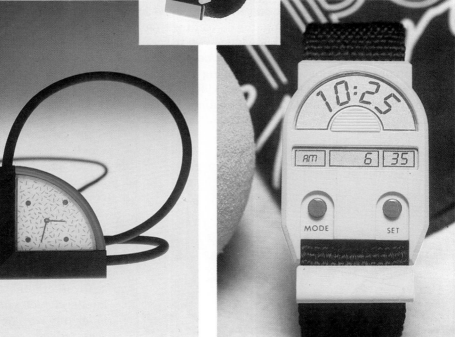

Mechanical Civil Aeronautical Electrical Automobile Electronic
Engineering Design

Typical project briefs

- Investigate domestic pumps. Look at those which are purchased as part of a product such as toothpaste or a window cleaner, those which are designed to be refilled such as garden sprays, and those which pump air such as bicycle pumps. Select one in each category and produce annotated/dynamic visual aids to show how each works. From your investigations produce some ideas for new applications. Develop one of these into a design proposal.

- Design and make a pop-up book which illustrates dynamically four ways in which energy can be generated.

- Use Ordnance Survey or AA maps to investigate road intersections between major roads such as motorways and trunk roads. Build up a dossier of the various ways in which traffic can change from one route to another. Select two major towns which are currently not joined by motorways (maximum distance apart of 40 miles). Make a proposal for a route for a motorway to link the towns. Design in detail three of the intersections.

- Designing to fail — engineers often design an item to fracture or break under certain loadings as a safety procedure. The electrical fuse is a good example; another is the illuminated polyethylene road bollard held in place by four nylon pins which shear when it is hit by a vehicle. Produce an explanatory leaflet explaining this concept with a range of examples. Put the knowledge you have acquired to good use by applying this concept to a potentially dangerous situation, making it safer. Alternatively it may be possible to modify a design in this way to make replacement cheaper.

- Collapsible structures serve a number of purposes, such as making an object more compact so that it can be transported easily or stored more efficiently. The umbrella is a good example of a mechanical solution, a li-lo of a pneumatic solution. Find out as much as you can about structures of this type and then redesign a product which might be improved or given a new market appeal from this kind of approach. For example, a wheelbarrow is a bulky object and often takes up a lot of space in a garden shed — how might this problem be solved?

- Aerodynamics is the science of air in motion. Make a study of four examples where the engineer has had to overcome the resistance of the atmosphere to improve either the performance or the safety of a design. Your examples should be as varied as possible, such as one involving flight, another land- or water-based movement, the effect of air movement on buildings and on sporting performance. An airline company is going to give away a paper glider as part of a promotion campaign. Design the glider and produce the final artwork of your design which exploits the company's corporate identity.

- Your home is a complex system. There are a number of inputs such as water, electricity, gas etc. which enable you and your family to live in an environment which can be controlled to meet your needs. Produce a series of diagrams to illustrate the various elements of these systems. How are the various inputs regulated? Select one and make a detailed study of how the inputs are controlled and measured, and what outputs result. Conduct a survey to establish if this resource could be used more economically. Produce a report for your parents detailing what might be done to reduce their bill for the utility you have selected.

- The diagram shows the original patent drawing for a food mixer of 1906. Make a study of the consumer products which have been designed this century and the effect which they have had on the way in which food has been prepared in the home. Pay particular attention to the changing technologies and how they have been incorporated into these products. Produce your study in graphical form. Are there activities in the kitchen which could be carried out more efficiently with power assistance or the design of a new gadget?

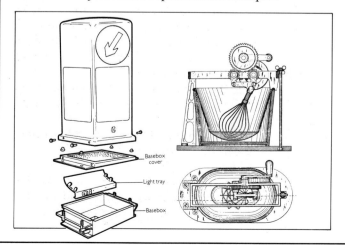

Basebox cover

Light tray

Basebox

Furniture Design
Technical Illustration
Product Design 3-D Design

Typical project briefs

- Select one of the following consumer products: compact cameras, steam irons, or personal music centres. Choose four examples and carry out a product analysis on each one. Produce a set of criteria which you believe are essential for the product you have chosen — a detailed specification. Design a solution which meets your criteria. Model your solution in expanded foam. Produce a cardboard point-of-sale display system for your design.

- Make a study of handles. Compile a report of at least 20 handles, critically analysing each in terms of their form and function. Describe the manufacturing processes involved in the production of each handle. With the information gained, design and model handles for one of the following: a set of kitchen utensils, a range of paint brushes or a canteen of cutlery. Produce presentation drawings to illustrate your design in context, and working drawings indicating the material and method of manufacture.

- 'The technology is available to design a vacuum cleaner with electrical sensors and spatial memory — one which will clean when everybody is at work. It may modify our domestic layout and habits, but what price an appliance which conquers the final drudgery barrier and boldly goes where no cleaners have gone before.' (John Almond, Design Magazine)

  Other criticisms of vacuum cleaners might be noise, poor storage of hoses, tools and cables. This is a good starting point for a design project.

- Investigate the requirements of school furniture, in both classrooms and specialist areas. How well does the furniture in your school fit the bill? Select the area which you feel is most poorly equipped. Design furniture which you think would meet the needs of the staff and the pupils. Model your design at an appropriate scale and produce working drawings showing the construction methods.

- Street furniture is often vandalized. Carry out a survey of street furniture in your town, paying particular attention to materials and construction, and how effective the designs are in withstanding vandalism. Design a range of street furniture and model it in an appropriate environment.

- A major high street fashion retailer requires a new storage and display system. The shop is unisex and the same system is to be used throughout. Before attempting to satisfy this brief, do some research in the high street and look at what is already on offer. Produce a scale model of your solution.

- Sporting equipment has in recent years become redesigned to improve both performance and appearance. Select a particular sport and detail the changes which have taken place in the past ten years. One of the leading manufacturers has decided to produce a small booklet describing these changes and making predictions about what might happen in the future. The booklet is to be A5 and will consist of 12 pages. Using your research, produce a dummy of the booklet.

- The elderly section of our society is expanding the most rapidly. The majority of domestic environments are designed for the fit and healthy. The same can be said of the products we use. Carry out research into the problems the elderly face in using either kitchens or bathrooms, or maintaining their gardens. Produce recommendations of how these areas and the tools and appliances found there might be adapted to make them more user-friendly for the old. Focus on a particular problem and produce a design solution to improve it.

- Design a range of bathroom and cloakroom accessories to be produced by injection moulding. Full working drawings should be made of your designs and exact prototype models made of your solutions.

- A DIY magazine is embarking on a series of articles which will give their readers the plans for a series of items of furniture which can be made out of a sheet of 20 mm MDF (medium density fibreboard). Design an item of furniture which could be made solely from this sheet material plus the appropriate fixings. Once designed and modelled, produce the plans and instructions which would appear in the magazine.

- Flashing LEDs can be seen in the dark at least half a mile away. As such, they can be used as warning or location devices. Develop a product which exploits this and produce an exact working model of your solution. An example might be a locating device for mountaineers lost or injured on the mountains.

PRESENTATION AND EVALUATION

Presentation tips

The way in which an individual drawing is presented will add greatly to its impact. You have already seen in Unit 3 the various ways in which a presentation drawing can be enhanced by adding a backdrop. There are a good many examples throughout the book of how to improve the presentation of your drawings. Here are a few additional tricks which you might try.

One of the best ways of picking up ideas is to look at the way in which other designers have presented solutions. On these two pages there are a range of examples. Look at the cover of *Design* magazine shown on this page. There are a number of simple ideas worth considering. They can help to make drawings appear dynamic.

1 The graphic illusion of making something appear as if it is pinned into your report can be achieved. This is easily done by drawing pins as they would appear. It is important to add the shadow. Mapping pins, which are coloured spheres, are easy to render but any type of pin can be used. Look at the other examples.

   A similar effect can be achieved by implying that a drawing is held down using tape.

2 The turned-down corner has also been used on the magazine cover. Used just as often is a turned-up corner. Both help to heighten the graphic image. Shading helps to convey an impression of three dimensions. The sequential drawings show how this has been achieved.

Splashing out: bathrooms of the future

3 There are many small details worth looking at, for example the shadow behind the picture of the traditional rubber duck makes it stand out from the page.

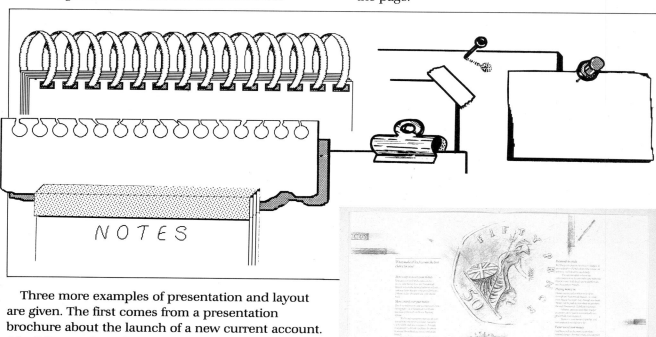

NOTES

Three more examples of presentation and layout are given. The first comes from a presentation brochure about the launch of a new current account. A building society, the Nationwide Anglia, commissioned this booklet when it became the first building society to offer investors the possibility of using the building society like a bank. Careful layout, variety of paper and illustrations reminiscent of brass rubbings help create a highly sophisticated appeal.

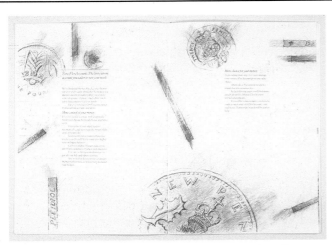

The second is the 1986 annual report of Cadbury Schweppes. The report must present to the shareholders a precise picture of the company's performance during the past financial year. The majority of designers use photographs to illustrate these reports. As you can see, this report uses illustrations which have a painting look to them. They look a bit like pointillist paintings of the nineteenth century, yet they also have a likeness to computer graphics, based on illuminated pixels of light. This approach has helped enhance the image of the ordinary products, bringing a fresh approach to what is often a stereotyped document.

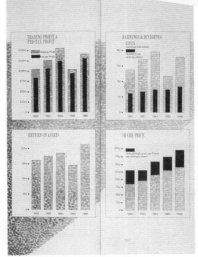

On 5th January 1987, Schweppes and Coca-Cola joined forces in Great Britain to create the country's largest soft drinks business.

The third example is the publicity brochure for a new car. The Isuzu Piazza Turbo was launched in the UK in the summer of 1986. Although a Japanese car, it had been designed by a famous Italian designer, Giugiaro. The design consultancy given the task of producing the promotional literature decided to exploit the designer aspect of the car. The brochure illustrates the design process, making the most of designer's sketches and tools such as pencils and fine-line pens. As the brochure and the design process progress, the pencils and erasers get progressively worn down.

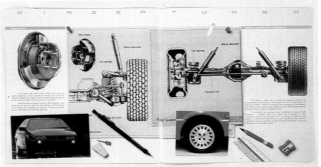

Page layout

Any piece of two-dimensional work which sets out to communicate an idea or a message to someone must be organized. This is referred to as page layout. All books, brochures, magazines and exhibition panels have been carefully thought out prior to being produced. The graphic designer uses a range of technical terms to describe the elements on a page. Before starting work on individual pages the guidelines controlling each of these elements will have been determined. This ensures that the book or exhibition will have a look of unity.

The design of text

A **heading** is the main title introducing a new chapter or subject. **Subheads** define the start of new sections within the main chapter. **Text** is the ordinary words on the page, often called the **copy** before being typeset. A **caption** is text which describes a visual element.

The size of type is usually expressed in points. The size of text will diminish with its importance. Headings will have the highest point size and the text will probably be the smallest. Typesize must be specified along with the selected character font — the style of the lettering. Text can also be justified or unjustified. If you are not sure what this means, look at the examples. The boldness of a typeface is referred to as its weight. Typefaces can also be italicized, shown in outline, or with a shadow.

Visuals

An **illustration** is a hand-produced picture or diagram. **Rules** are vertical and horizontal lines used to divide up the content. A **box** is a rule which completely surrounds an element of text, illustration or photograph. **Margins** are the blank area which surrounds the pictures and words. **Bleed** happens when an illustration or photograph goes over the margin and off the page. **Bullets** are dots used to highlight points in the text.

When you are starting work on any project it is a good idea to think about layout before you get started. A design folio will be much improved with consistent attention to detail.

Layout grids

The next step is to design a layout grid. This serves as a framework for the designer. It determines the width of blocks of text and visuals. The simplest grid is a single column. This is generally used for novels. Reports may have one, two or three columns, whilst newspapers are the most complex having as many as eight columns. It is a good idea to keep text in columns, but visual material can cross columns and bleed into the margin and off the page. This will give pages a more lively look. Draw a grid out accurately. If possible use it on a lightbox with the final sheet of your report on top. Juggle the various elements around to find the best arrangement.

TEXT

A Point is a measure of size used in typesetting: there are 12 points in a Pica. One point is about 1/72 of an inch.

font	point size
Helvetica	24
Helvetica	18
Helvetica	14
Helvetica	12
Helvetica	10
Helvetica	9

style

Helvetica plain
Helvetica bold
Helvetica italic
Helvetica outline
Helvetica shadow

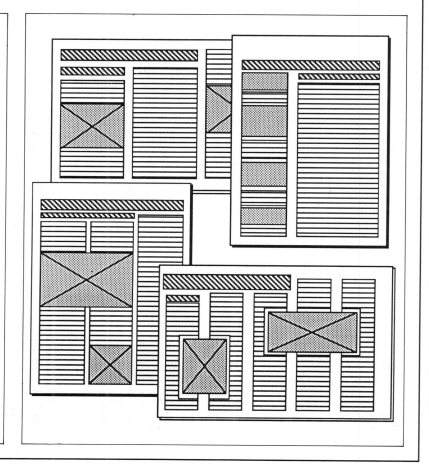

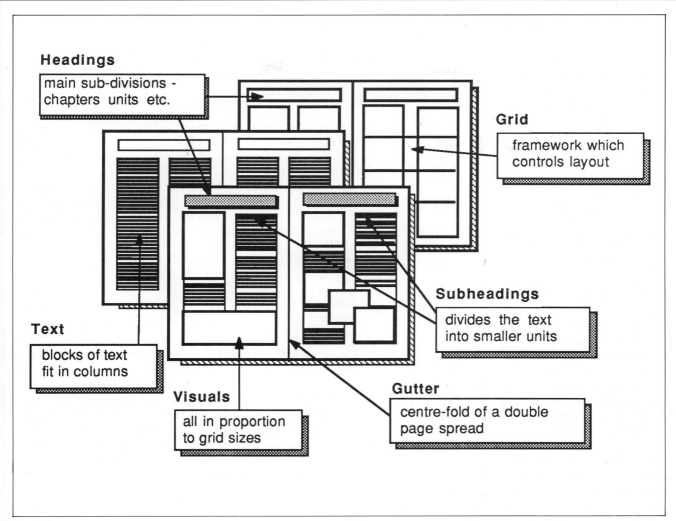

Headings
main sub-divisions - chapters units etc.

Grid
framework which controls layout

Text
blocks of text fit in columns

Subheadings
divides the text into smaller units

Visuals
all in proportion to grid sizes

Gutter
centre-fold of a double page spread

Compiling a design report

Designing is about finding the best solutions to problems. When working for a client it is essential that a designer presents his or her work well. It must be easy to understand and follow. The content must be logical and reasons for decisions clearly explained. Every professional designer sets out to present projects as professionally as possible, as this helps to create a feeling of confidence in the client's mind. You may be designing for a real client but the GCSE examiner is also very much a client of your work. The examiner in the first instance is the class teacher, but then it is quite likely that an external examiner will also look at your major project. Your report will have a lot of individual characteristics to it. Do not produce your report to a formula, otherwise it will appear dull and rather staid. However, try to take the following ten points into account:

- Decide on a size and format for the two-dimensional aspect of the project.
- Develop a page layout or style to include borders, headings etc.
- Keep all your work once you start your project. Try to ensure it does not become dog-eared and scruffy.

- Arrange your work in a sequential manner so that the stages which you went through can be easily identified. When completed, number the pages.
- Give the sections headings and produce an index or reference system so that particular aspects of your project can be easily found if required.
- The headings may well follow the stages in a design project:
  Identifying the problem/Investigation/ Specification/Ideas/Development/Realization/ Testing and evaluation
- Produce a cover which reflects the content of your project.
- Write a synopsis — a short statement which will outline what your project is about, how you tackled it and the level of success you achieved. This enables anybody to get a quick overview of your work.
- Make sure that all mock-ups, models and three-dimensional work are referred to in the text so that they can be fitted into the context of the project.
- Finally complete an honest and fair evaluation of your work, your success and your failures, the lessons you've learnt and the problems you've solved. If you have been tackling a project for a client, ask them to comment on the quality of your solution and include their response.

Students' examples

On this page there are four examples of projects undertaken by students. In each case examples are shown of the project so you can see the care taken with layout and presentation.

1 Pauline undertook a study of how time is measured for this project. She decided to use coloured pencils for the project as she felt these had the right visual quality given the subject matter of her project. From a study of the history of telling time the project developed into the design and manufacture of a sundial and a water clock.

2 Tim set out to do a packaging project on an Easter egg. After research of what was currently being sold he developed some new and imaginative ideas and produced a well organized and efficient project folder.

3 Geoff was interested in storage in the home, in particular shelving systems which could be expanded as required and could be easily adjusted. You can see how his ideas evolved until he produced a solution which needed to be modelled to prove whether it worked. The idea was then developed so that limited production could be undertaken at a later date.

4 Andrea undertook a project to redesign a telephone. Since the privatization of British Telecom the variety of handsets available to the consumer has increased dramatically. After exploring what is currently available, Andrea set about designing one herself. You can see that her ideas have been put together with great care and presented in an attractive yet informative way.

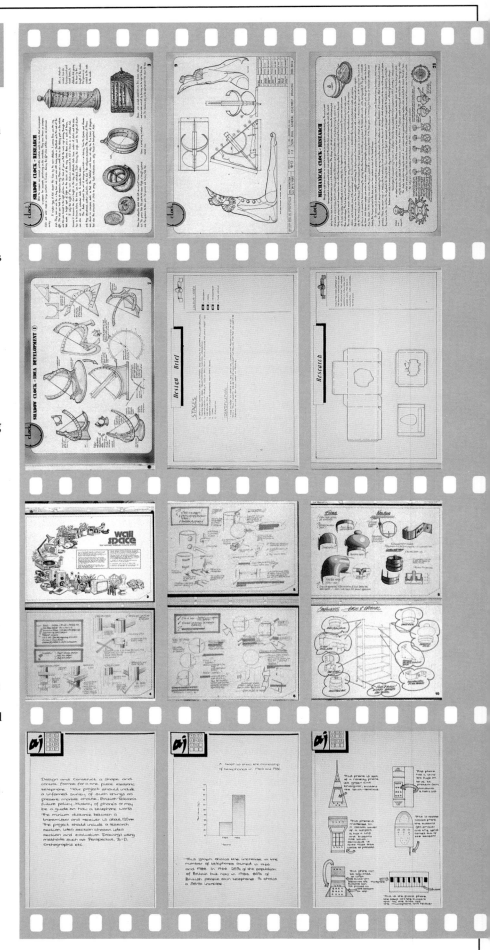

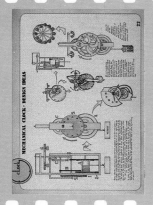

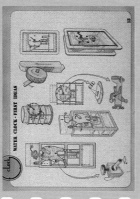

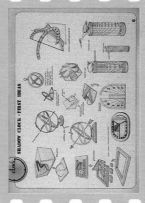

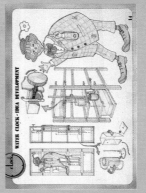

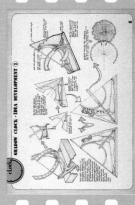

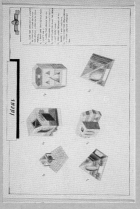

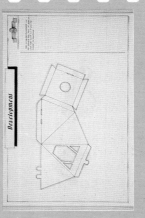

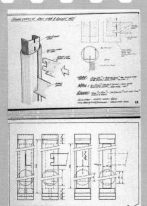

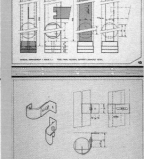

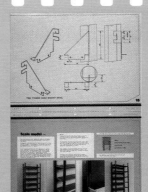

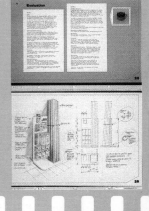

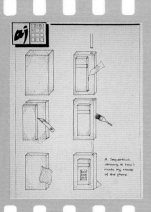

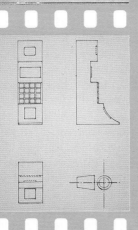

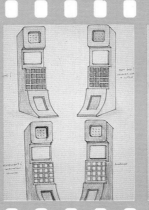

Evaluating your work

At the end of every project you will have been faced with the task of evaluating your work to assess how successful it is. It is always difficult to be dispassionate about a project which has involved you in a great deal of time and effort. We are all sensitive to criticism of things that mean a great deal to us. You will have gained experience in assessing your own work and that of others throughout the course. You will know how important it is to try and encourage others with your comments, to be positive whilst still being honest. Remember to apply the same principle to your own work. Comment on the things which have gone well as well as those on which you might improve.

It is a good idea to separate the two aspects — personal evaluation of your own performance, and evaluation of the proposed solution. It is quite likely that you might work very hard, be extremely conscientious and produce an average solution. Alternatively, you may have been a bit lazy, let the project drift but in the end had an inspiration and come up with a very good idea. We shall deal with solution evaluation first of all.

Evaluating a solution

You should always have something to judge your final result against. You will have started with a brief and this will have been expanded into a specification — a set of criteria which you have attempted to meet. You have been constantly referring to this to test ideas and check out all possible solutions. The first step then is to go through the specification and see how close you've come to meeting it.

Testing

However detailed a specification might be, it is not the end of the story. Whatever is involved it must be tested to see if it really does the job for which it is intended. In any situation there are four different types of people: designer, maker, client, user. They could all be the same person, or they could all be different. If I set out to design a wardrobe for my bedroom I am the client, I will design it and make it and when finished I will use it. A very different situation is this book. The client is the publisher, Century Hutchinson. They commissioned me to design and write it, printers to make it, and you are the user. This is a far more complex chain in which several of those involved never even meet.

Your project will fit into one of four categories, from the simplest where you might design and make something for yourself, to the most complex, similar to the production of this book.

The client or the user should be involved in the testing if possible. It may well have to be someone who represents them and can put themselves in the client's position. Do not be surprised if by the time they come to test something commissioned months or even weeks earlier they have changed their minds. For this reason you must maintain contact all the time with a client, otherwise you may be going in opposite directions.

Try to get written comments about the success of your product. Use questionnaires if you need an unbiased anonymous reaction. You can ask questions in three categories: function, aesthetic and economic.

Function questions might include:
- Does it do the task for which it is intended?
- Does it do it safely?
- Does it do it reliably?
- Will it continue to do it?

These questions consider performance, safety, reliability and durability.

Aesthetic questions might include:
- Does it have visual appeal?
- Does it fit in with its environment?
- Is it the right colour?
- Are the proportions satisfying?

These questions consider form, environment, colour and proportions.

Economic questions might include:
- Can it be produced economically?
- Does it give good value for money?
- Can it be priced competitively?
- Is it a valid use of resources?

These questions consider feasibility, value, competition and resources.

The questions will vary according to your project and the nature of the end product.

Personal evaluation

Assessing your own performance is bound to be more subjective than evaluating the end product. No doubt you will be helped by personal profile forms, which are a series of questions which will focus your attention on how you are progressing. These forms help you to learn from failings and capitalize on your positive attributes.

These forms are only of value if you can discuss them with someone else. The normal procedure is for you and your teacher to fill them in independently and then compare results and reach an agreement. The agreement should set you targets in your next project. If, for example, you have both identified that you find it difficult to meet deadlines, you may decide to break the next project down into a series of interim deadlines to make sure you do not fall behind. The whole process will help you to make the most of your own personal resources.

The form will probably ask you questions about the following aspects: responsibility, reliability, co-operation, perseverance, innovation, ingenuity, decisiveness and application.

In industry, commerce and all forms of employment, annual evaluation or assessment is becoming common. The objective is similar, to try to make sure that someone is as effective at their job as they can be. It is not just for the benefit of the employer, it is also to try and make sure that the employees are fulfilled, that their careers are progressing as they would wish and that they feel appreciated and rewarded for the work that they do. It is always better to discuss problems in an honest, open atmosphere than allow them to develop.

Exhibiting your work

Looking at a project report can be difficult, as it is often impossible to look at more than one page at a time. It is a good idea that any binding on a project is temporary or removable, so that your project can be exhibited. You may be asked to mount your exhibition for the visiting examiner or for a school display. Exhibitions need to be designed as carefully as everything else. Use your imagination. You can do a great deal with cheap and discarded materials. They may need some coats of emulsion to disguise their identity, but packing cases and boxes can be used in an infinite number of ways!

Before you start

Although the exhibition is important, remember that you will want your drawings after the exhibition is finished, so you must firstly think about how they can be protected.

If your drawings are going to be pinned up, reinforce the corners to prevent their being torn. You can purchase ring reinforcements, tabs and discs, and holes can be punched with an eyeletter. A simple method is to reinforce the back of each sheet with masking tape. There are a wide range of pins available. Coloured mapping pins are perhaps the best as they can be colour co-ordinated with your drawings. Dress-making pins are almost invisible if used carefully. Try to always push the pin through the same point on each drawing — the intersection of the border, for example.

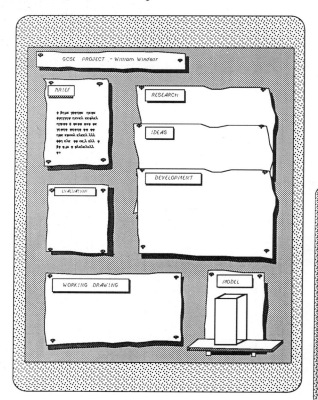

Selecting drawings

Very rarely is it possible to exhibit all your work — a selection will have to be made. Choose a range of drawings which tells the best story — those which illustrate the developmental stages most clearly. Once you have made a selection check it out with a friend or your teacher.

Mounting drawings

It is always a good idea to mount drawings on coloured paper. It will help to unify your work and make it stand out from other work on display. The paper will act as a frame and enhance the quality of your work. Make sure your work is mounted accurately:

- Select your mounting paper carefully, it should always be plain and should not detract from the work.
- Firstly position the drawing precisely on the coloured paper.
- Mark the position of the corners in pencil so they will not be seen when the drawing is glued down.
- Spraymount the drawing following the instructions on the can. Most spraymounts allow for repositioning.

Displaying your work

Start by establishing sight lines. If it is a large exhibition try to make sure everyone sticks to these lines, particularly for sheets which require reading. Remember, sight lines set the top and bottom of the display area, they should enable visitors to view exhibits without craning their necks or bending down.

Treat your display as a unit. Firstly, sketch possible layouts, always ensuring that drawings relate in groups. This helps the visitor to concentrate on a particular aspect. It is rather boring to space drawings regularly and evenly. When you have decided on the layout check that no additional information is required. You may need to add some additional notes or arrows — exhibitions must be self-explanatory! Remember to include titles and

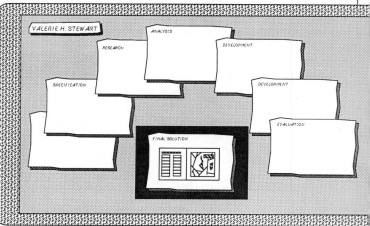

headings within your layout. They must be prepared specially and should be eyecatching.

Lightweight models can be incorporated into a display. Simple mounting brackets can be made out of card which can be pinned to the wall. Reflective card used as a background can really set off a model. Alternatively, models can be suspended using fishing line. This makes them appear as if they are floating in space.

Heavier models will have to be placed on a plinth or table. Most surfaces are too low, so think about placing a plinth on a table to bring it within the sight lines of the exhibition. Use coloured paper to make the surfaces part of the whole display. If there are particular features of a model referred to in the flat artwork, use cotton lines to link them.

Mounting an exhibition is a design problem. It requires planning and time if it is to be a success. Make sure you take a photographic record as exhibitions do not last long. The photographs should go into your folder of work. Finally, remember to take your work down as carefully as you put it up. Drawings, which can take many hours to do, are easily torn or damaged.

In this unit there is a representative sample of questions taken from the first GCSE examinations held in the summer of 1988. There are questions from all the examination boards. At the end of each question the abbreviated name of the board which set the question is given:

London and East Anglian Group	**LEAG**
Midland Examining Group	**MEG**
Northern Examining Association	**NEA**
Northern Ireland Schools Examining Council	**NISEC**
Southern Examining Group	**SEG**
Welsh Joint Education Council	**WJEC**

The marks allocated for each question are also given. These marks are not directly comparable as the pattern of marking varies from board to board. The questions become more difficult and involved as you progress through the unit. In general the questions on each page cover a similar topic, for example the questions on this page deal with statistical information.

1 The different types of sales in a music shop are given, as percentages, in the table below.

Item	% of sales
Records	40
Cassettes	30
Compact discs	15
Video cassettes	10
Memorabilia	5
Total	**100**

a The graphic form of data representation shows the percentage sales of records.
  i Copy and complete the representation showing the other types of sales.
  ii Copy and complete the key. (Colour may be used.)
b The number of records sold in the music shop was 24 000. This is shown in another form of data representation.
Copy and complete this representation by:
  i adding suitable divisions on the scale line;
  ii showing the number of cassettes, compact discs, video cassettes and memorabilia sold. (Use the same key as in **a**.)   *(20 marks)* (SEG)

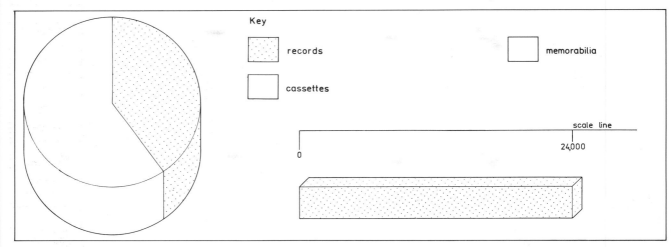

Key — records, cassettes, memorabilia

scale line   0   24,000

2 An Historical Atlas needs an illustration to show the development of pig iron output of South Wales for the period 1770 to 1870, shown as a proportion of total British production.

Figures for the period are as follows:
Pig Iron Output of South Wales.

Design and draw a suitable two- or three-dimensional graph, chart or diagram to illustrate the given figures for the atlas.

Marks will be given for the effective use of colour and/or shading.   *(13 marks)* (WJEC)

Year	South Wales output x 1000 tons	Total British output x 1000 tons	South Wales output as a percentage of total British output
1770	48	276	17%
1820	182	455	40%
1840	505	1402	36%
1850	706	2017	35%
1870	969	3876	25%

3 A pupil has started a project in which photographic equipment is being investigated and has made the first schematic sketch of the circuit of a slide projector. The sketch is shown in the figure.

The BS symbols for each of the components except the fan are given.

a Design a suitable symbol to represent a fan.
(2 marks)

b Using the symbols given and the one you have designed draw a formal circuit diagram of the circuit illustrated. *(4 marks)* (MEG)

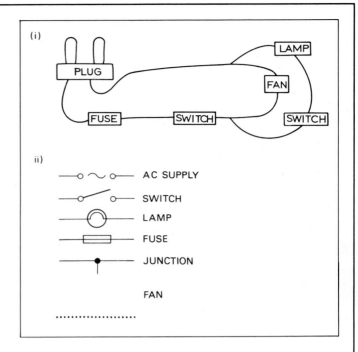

(i)

ii)

— AC SUPPLY

— SWITCH

— LAMP

— FUSE

— JUNCTION

FAN

....

4 The sketch shows a domestic water system consisting of a cold water supply tank (CWS) and a hot water supply tank (HWS), feeding a WC, a heated towel rail and a shower.

Using the symbols given, complete the diagram of the system below. *(10 marks)* (WJEC)

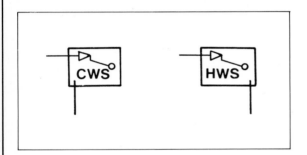

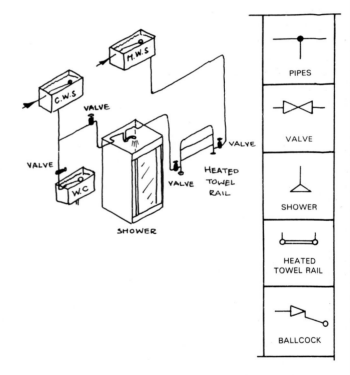

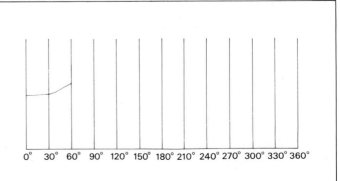

PIPES

VALVE

SHOWER

HEATED TOWEL RAIL

BALLCOCK

5 The figure shows the outline of a plate cam. The position of a knife edge follower is shown. The cam rotates in a clockwise direction.

The start of an angle/displacement graph is given. Copy and complete the graph, then measure and state the greatest distance the follower rises above the horizontal axis of the graph.
(8 marks) (MEG)

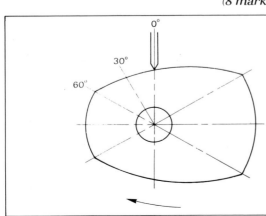

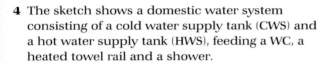

0° 30° 60° 90° 120° 150° 180° 210° 240° 270° 300° 330° 360°

6 The illustration of the car given below is to be reproduced within a rectangle measuring 150 × 80.

Using a grid, enlarge the drawing in a rectangle of the given size. *(6 marks)* (NEA)

7 Two orthographic views of a tap are shown.
   a Make a freehand pictorial sketch of the tap. *(16 marks)*
   b Add appropriate shading and/or colour to your sketch. *(8 marks)* (MEG)

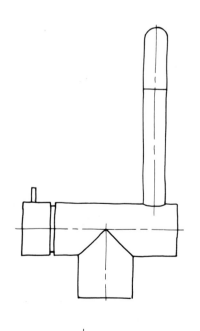

8 Two symbols are shown from a series produced for one of the Olympic Games.

The symbols represent track events and rowing.

Produce a symbol to represent swimming which is in the same style as those given. You should present your final solution in a rectangle of 120 x 60 mm. *(5 marks)* (NEA)

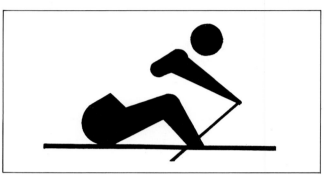

9 Television and television magazines use graphic symbols for instant subject identification.

The drawings show four sporting examples.

Select **two** topics from the following list:
   Car rallying; DIY; Space; Politics; Snooker; Food; Travel.

Design a graphic symbol for **each** of the topics you have chosen.

The outline of the symbols may be any shape and approximately 100 mm high.

(Add single-colour rendering to your final solutions.) *(25 marks)* (SEG)

10 An entry for a competition to design a collecting box for the Red Cross has been received in the form of an orthographic drawing as shown below. The design can be interpreted in a number of different ways.

Make pictorial freehand sketches which show two of these interpretations. *(6 marks)* (MEG)

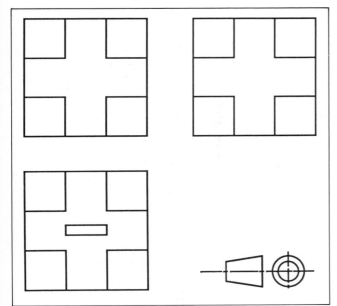

11 As part of an advertising campaign a company called Universal Packaging are giving away small globes of the world packaged in a box, a pictorial view of which is shown below.

a Construct a development (net) of the box including all necessary flaps and glue tabs. You must be able to open and close the top of the box.

b Draw, to suitable size, the letters U and P on to the development so that when the box is folded the letters will appear in the positions shown in the pictorial view. *(8 marks)* (MEG)

12 The manufacturers of the flower vase, shown in the orthographic drawing below, require a box to be designed in which the vase can be packaged. They have requested that

  i the box should be made from single piece of card;

  ii it should be of the shape shown in the isometric drawing;

  iii it should have one side that opens to allow the vase to be removed.

A sketch of a design which was rejected is shown on the right.

a Comment on why the design was rejected.

b Sketch, in pictorial form, similar to that given, two suitable designs for the box.

c Select one of the designs and draw, using a scale of 1:2, a development of the box. The drawing should include all the necessary flaps and glue tabs to make the box. These parts should be labelled on your drawing.

(16 marks) (SEG)

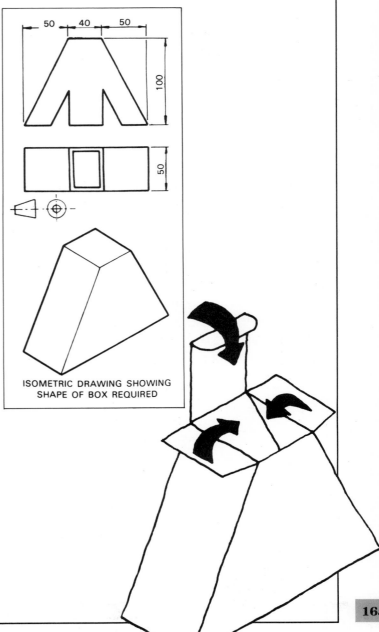

ISOMETRIC DRAWING SHOWING SHAPE OF BOX REQUIRED

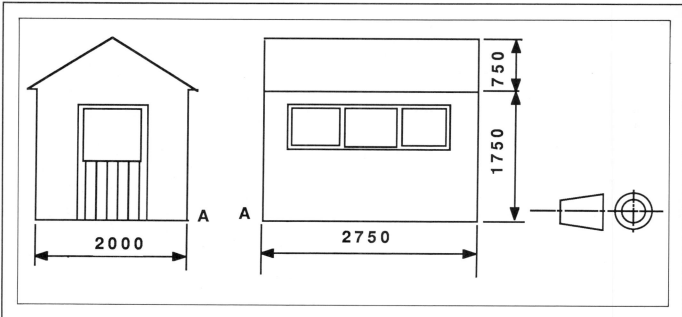

13 The orthographic drawing shows details of a garden shed.

 a Draw, to a suitable scale, an estimated perspective view of the shed. Corner **A** should be the lowest point on your drawing.

 b Add suitable colour or shading to your drawing. *(10 marks)* (LEAG)

14 Orthographic views of a swimming pool are given. The pool has a wooden frame which is used to cover the pool in the winter.

Draw to a suitable scale, a **pictorial** view of the pool and frame in a form suitable for inclusion in an advertising brochure. Add to the view, features such as pool-side seats, a slide and entrance steps which will enhance the illustration. Show the pool filled with water to the level of the underside of the concrete slabs.

Dimensions and details not given are left to your discretion.

Marks will be given for the effective use of colour and/or shading. *(20 marks)* (WJEC)

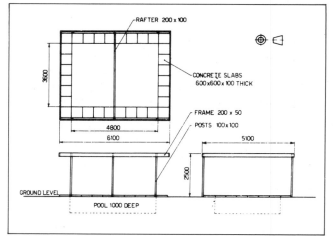

15 Three of the components from a constructional kit for young children are shown assembled in the full size orthographic views. The square joining piece passes right through the other two components.

 a Suggest a suitable material for the manufacture of the pieces. *(1 mark)*

 b Sketch an exploded isometric view of the three pieces starting at bottom left with the cylinder. *(7 marks)* (MEG)

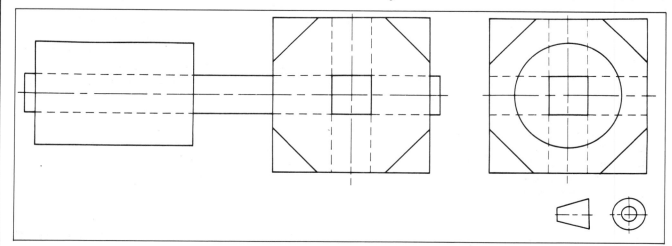

16 The London underground railway map is a classic example of graphic design. On the map the impact of basic information and the sequence of stations are more important than precise distances and direction.

Opposite is a map in conventional form showing the towns linked by railway.

Make a map, in the London Underground style, showing **all** the different routes from **Birmingham** to **Exeter**.

(Marks will be awarded for the effective use of colour and the inclusion of a key.)

(25 marks) (SEG)

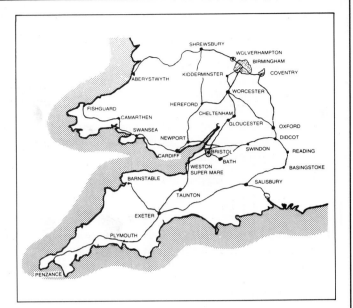

17 The sketch plan of a hospital campus is given below. Also given is a view of a sign to be placed at the entrance of the hospital in the position indicated on the sketch.

Complete the view of the sign by using instruments to draw the layout of the buildings and roads of the hospital, in a way which may help visitors find their way about. Your view of the sign should measure 195 mm x 120 mm.

Print **CAR PARK** and **MEDICAL WARDS** only in appropriate positions on your diagram, and include arrows showing the way round the island to the car park. *(14 marks)* (WJEC)

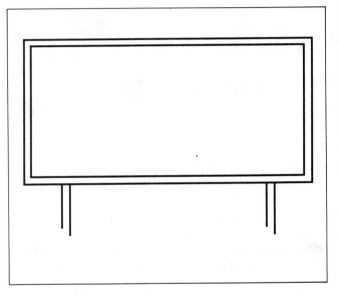

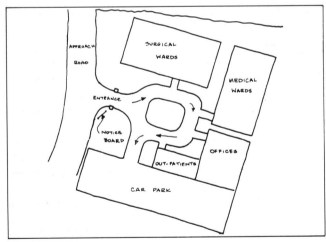

18 A bus company, operating long-distance journeys, is to provide passengers with a packaged meal in order to avoid stopping en route for refreshments.

Each meal is to be packed in a rigid disposable container which must not exceed 300 mm long by 225 mm wide and 75 mm high. The following items are to be included in separate compartments in the container:

  i a small wrapped meat pie;
  ii sandwiches, which need a space 140 mm by 75 mm by 65 mm deep;
  iii a small quantity of salad;
  iv a trifle, which needs a space 90 mm by 55 mm by 50 mm deep;
  v an apple;
  vi a plastic cup with a handle; overall height 70 mm by 65 mm diameter;
  vii sachets of salt, pepper and sugar which fit in a single compartment;
  viii a small knife, fork and teaspoon wrapped in a paper serviette.

In use the container will have a plastic cover but this is not to be shown in your answer.

a make at least **two** design sketches of a suitable container;
b state the material from which the container is to be made;
c **sketch freehand**, approximately **half full size**, a **pictorial** view of the container with the cup in its compartment.

Do **not** draw the food or the other items listed.

Do **not** use colour in answering this question.

(13 marks) (WJEC)

19 The drawing shows details of part of a
   typewriter, together with a set of graphical
   symbols for representing the levers and linkages
   from a mechanical system.

   a Select from the given symbols and **sketch
   freehand** a suitable representation of the
   typewriter details.

   b Using instruments and in reasonable
   proportion re-draw your representation for the
   typewriter details.

   Make your drawing about twice the size of the
   one given.   *(15 marks)* (LEAG)

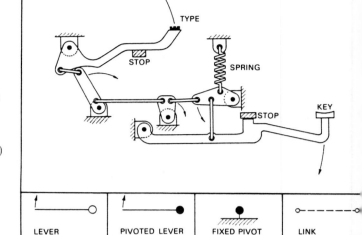

20 A company called Computer Installations wants
   to produce a gift for customers which is to be
   made from 3 mm acrylic sheet. You are required
   to produce a design for a desk note-pad holder
   for this purpose. The size of the note-pad is given
   (right).

   a Produce preliminary sketches of three
   alternatives.   *(6 marks)*

   b Select one and illustrate the method of making
   it.   *(3 marks)*

   c Produce a large, colour rendered, pictorial
   drawing of your selected idea. This drawing
   should be of a quality which could be shown
   to the client to persuade him to adopt your
   idea.   *(5 marks)* (NEA)

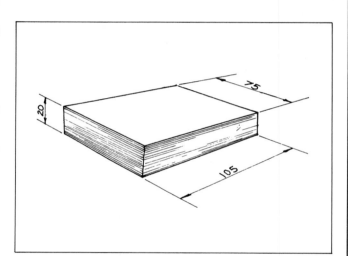

21 The drawing (bottom right) shows a pictorial view
   of the basic parts of a **toy roundabout**.

   The mechanical parts are to be contained within
   the box.

   a By means of sketches and notes design a
   suitable handle, to be joined to the shaft, so
   that it can be turned in a clockwise direction.

   b By means of sketches and notes show how the
   rotary motion of the handle is transmitted
   through a right angle to make the roundabout
   turn.

   c By means of sketches and notes show how one
   turn of the handle will make the roundabout
   turn four times.

   Marks will be awarded for suitable colour
   and/or shading.   *(15 marks)* (SEG)

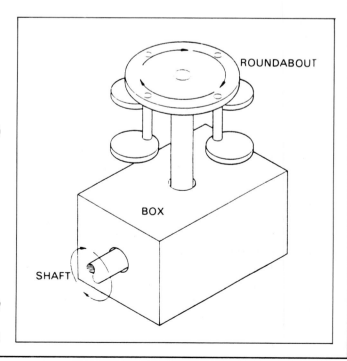

22 Assume that you have been asked to produce
   pictorial illustrations, with notes, to show pupils
   in junior forms what the following are;
   i Belt drive
   ii Rack and pinion

   a Produce good quality, large, clear drawings for
   this purpose. You should keep the drawings
   simple so that you can produce high quality
   illustrations. You may use drawing aids to help
   improve the drawings.   *(10 marks)*

   b Illustrate **one** mechanism in a working
   situation.   *(5 marks)* (NEA)

23 Details are given of an existing design for a paved patio. Modifications need to be made to this design so that a person in a wheel chair would be able to use both levels of the patio and have access to the lawn.

a Make a **freehand sketch, in pictorial form**, showing the modifications that you would make to the patio. Only the back wall of the house should be included in your sketch.

b Add to your sketch a suitably positioned flower bed which a disabled person could easily work on whilst in a wheel chair. *(15 marks)* (LEAG)

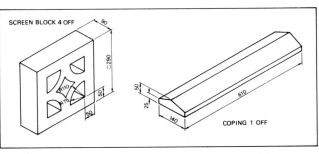

PAVED AREA ON TWO LEVELS
STEPS DOWN TO LAWN
LAWN LEVEL

24 A self-build kit for a barbecue consists of the following materials:

60 bricks;
1 sheet plate;
1 piece of wire mesh.

The drawings show the sizes of these components.
(The bricks are to be assembled without mortar.)

Instructions for building the barbecue are as follows.

i Arrange five bricks on a flat surface in a ⌐‾‾¬ shape measuring 645 mm by 315 mm.

ii Build on this foundation until the structure is eight bricks high.

iii Position the plate on top of the structure.

iv Add another two courses of bricks.

v Position the wire mesh on the bricks.

vi Add another two courses of bricks.

For advertising purposes a view of the assembled barbecue is required. This is to appear on the outside of the box which contains the materials and assembly instructions. The view is to be reproduced, photographically, from an original.

a Draw, using instruments, a **pictorial view** of the completed barbecue.

b Add two-colour rendering to your drawing.
(18 marks) (SEG)

25 Details are given of some of the pieces required to build a decorative garden wall. These pieces are joined in the following way.

The three pilasters are joined together one on top of another with a 10 mm mortar joint between each. The cap is then added to the top with a 10 mm mortar joint. Two of the screen blocks slot into the pilasters, no mortar is used between the pilasters and screen blocks but there is a 10 mm mortar joint between each of the screen blocks. Further blocks are then added onto the sides of these first two blocks. Finally the coping is placed along the top of the screen blocks using a 10 mm mortar joint.

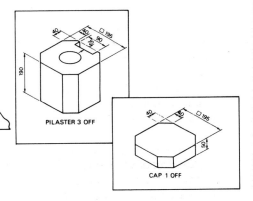

PILASTER 3 OFF

CAP 1 OFF

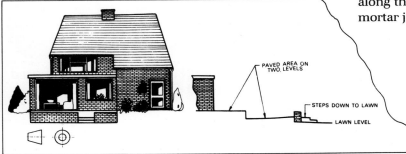

SCREEN BLOCK 4 OFF

COPING 1 OFF

a Using a scale of 1:5 draw an elevation showing the pieces assembled as described above and including all mortar joints. *(16 marks)*

b Use appropriate shading, colour and texture to represent the materials from which the wall is made. *(8 marks)* (MEG)

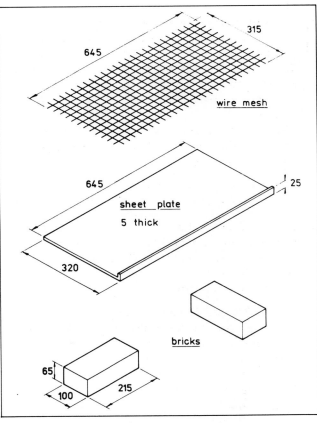

wire mesh

315
645

sheet plate
5 thick

645
320
25

bricks

65
100
215

26 As part of a campaign advertising holidays in Paris, a Travel Agent plans to give away a sheet containing a cut-out model of the Eiffel Tower. A partly finished orthographic drawing of the model is shown below. The model is to be made in four separate parts **A, B, C** and **D**.

a Using information from the given drawing add to the elevation a drawing of a suitably designed piece **A**.

b Make a sketch showing the development of piece **B**.

c Make a sketch showing the development of piece **C**.

d Make an accurate drawing of the development of piece **D**. Sizes for this drawing can be taken from the given elevation and plan. All construction should be clearly shown.

(15 marks) (LEAG)

27 The drawings show three stages of an **animated sequence** for the beginning of a television programme.

The letters of the word **shelf** in stage 1 are transformed into the outline of a shelf in stage 3.

a Prepare at least **three** preliminary sketches to explore possible ideas for the outline of the transformation needed to complete **stage 2** of the sequence.

b Take the best features of your ideas and develop a suitable design.

c Using instruments draw your design within the box for **stage 2**.

(The box should measure 145 mm x 55 mm.)

Do not add colour or shading to your drawings.

(15 marks) (LEAG)

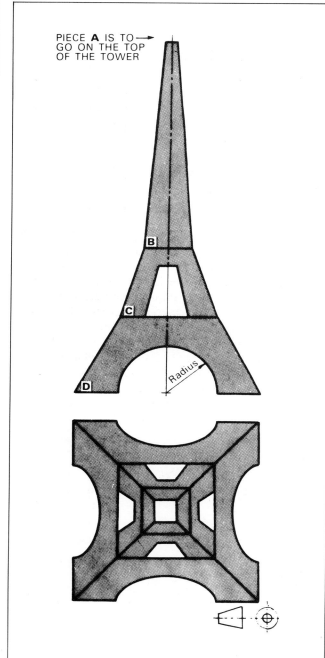

PIECE **A** IS TO →
GO ON THE TOP
OF THE TOWER

B

C

D

Radius

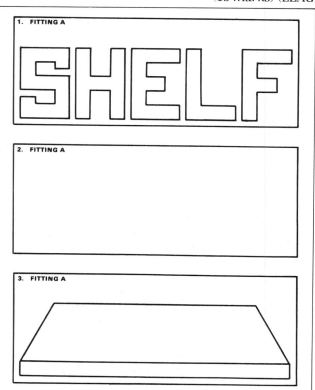

1. FITTING A

2. FITTING A

3. FITTING A

28 Fig. 1 shows a view of the eaves junction of a house with the top end of a ladder in the desired position for painting the facia and soffit boards. The dimensions of the ends of the ladder are shown in Fig. 2.

The ladder should not be placed against the gutter and if placed against the wall, painting the facia board would be dangerous.

NOTE: Neat sketches should be used to illustrate ideas and solutions to the design problems in parts **a**, **c** and **d**.

Formal drawings are required for part **b**.

a Sketch a device by which the ladder could be supported at the position shown in Fig. 1. The device may rest against the wall but should be securely attached to the latter. Safety is of paramount importance.

b Draw to an appropriate scale orthographic views of the device asked for in part **a**. Insert **four** important dimensions.

c Suggest by means of notes and sketches **one** method of ensuring that the lower end of the ladder does not slip while resting on the ground.

d Assuming that there will be occasions when the lower end of the ladder will be placed on a grass surface, sketch a means of preventing the ladder sinking into the ground.

(40 marks) (NISEC)

29 *A teacher of blind children has asked a CDT class to make sets of aids to counting and has discussed the project with the class. Together they have drawn up the following specifications.*

   i *The counting aids will all be the same size, made of wood with discs glued on to one surface to enable the pupils to count by sense of touch. Each block will be 100 mm square by 15 mm deep. The discs will be 20 mm in diameter and 6 mm thick.*

   ii *The maximum number of discs required on one block will be nine and these are to be arranged in a regular pattern of three rows of three discs.*

   iii *All other blocks of numbers from 1 to 8 shall have the centres of their discs based on the same grid pattern as that of the centres of the 9 disc block. A 3 disc and a 4 disc example are illustrated.*

   iv *A large number of blocks and a variety of layouts of discs for any given number will be required. The children would then be able, as well as counting, to use the blocks to play a game of matching pairs of identical blocks using their sense of touch.*

Taking account of the specifications given, you are to perform the following tasks.

a In a 100 mm square construct the plan of the 9 disc block. The spacing between each row of three in both directions has to be equal. The distance between the edge of the block and the

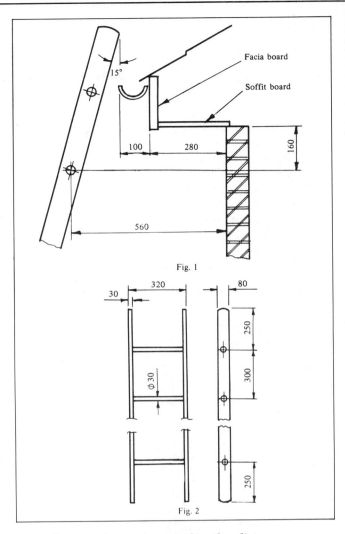

Fig. 1

Fig. 2

first row has to be equal to the distance between rows. *(8 marks)*

b Design a template which can be used to draw the position of any pattern for a given number of discs (from 1 to 9) on a prepared block. The template should include some means of locating it accurately on a block. A working drawing is not required but your sketches should show clearly the appearance of the template and how it will function. *(12 marks)*

c Plan a simple flow chart of a sequence of processes for making a block in the workshop.

The material provided is a 1 metre length of timber which has been machine planed to 100 mm x 15 mm. The 20 mm diameter discs have been purchased ready made for gluing to the block. *(12 marks)* (MEG)

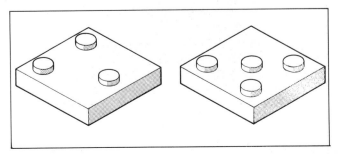

30 A new company, **Amalgamated Petroleum**, has been formed by the merging of two oil and petroleum distribution and sales companies. The new company will own a large number of service stations throughout the country.

As the company is anxious to develop a corporate identity, a logo is required. The logo is to appear on:

    tanker vehicles;
    oil cans;
    petrol pumps;
    letter headings;
    other advertising material.

a Produce design ideas and develop, to presentation quality, **two** alternative logos for consideration by the Board of Directors of the new company.

The designs must:
  i be appropriate to the new company;
  ii have overall shape and colour that are unique to petroleum sales;
  iii display a central motif that is distinctive of the company name and the nature of the company's products. *(50 marks)*

b Select the design you prefer and state why you feel that the shape, central motif, and colour scheme are particularly suitable for the new company. *(10 marks)*

The company has developed a new windscreen-washer fluid and intends to sell this in its service stations.

The intention is to market the product in a full range of sizes but, for promotional purposes, a special 28 ml (1 fl oz) sample size is to be introduced. In order to display the product to advantage a small display stand, to hold one container, is required. The stand is to be displayed on the counter at the point of sale.

The design must satisfy several requirements.

The stand must:
    be free-standing;
    be capable of being packed flat;
    show the name of the fluid and the company logo;
    include necessary information.

c Develop a suitable name for the windscreen-washer fluid. *(10 marks)*
d Design a display stand that would accommodate the 28 ml container. *(40 marks)*
e Using card, make a full-size prototype of the display stand. (Include all the necessary graphics from your design sketches.) *(40 marks)* (SEG)

31 The photograph shows a telephone. It is 180 mm long, 45 mm wide and 50 mm from back to front. The telephone is to be sold packed in a recess in a block of expanded polystyrene, so that it cannot move. The block of polystyrene then fits tightly in a cardboard box.

a **Sketch freehand** your design for a suitably shaped and sized block of polystyrene showing the recess for the telephone. Show the **three** principal dimensions of the block.
   Note
   i The side *A* of the telephone should be visible.
   ii There must be a suitable thickness of polystyrene all round the telephone.
   iii A recess is needed to pack the telephone cable.
   iv The buttons of the telephone need particular protection.
   v The telephone is to be made in a number of colours. Include holes in the block so that the colour of the telephone can be seen at each end of the box.

b Use instruments to draw a **scale 1:1** development of the box including gluing and other flaps, and the holes for colour identification.

c The telephone is sold by TELESTAR. On **two adjacent** sides of the development of the cardboard box, show your design for the way it is to be printed in order to attract customers. Your design should include:
   i the name of the manufacturer;
   ii logo/trademark for the company;
   iii information that the box contains a **one-piece telephone**;
   iv information that features of the telephone include:
   Push button operation
   Last number redial
   Mute button.

Marks will be given for the effective use of colour and/or shading. *(56 marks)* (WJEC)

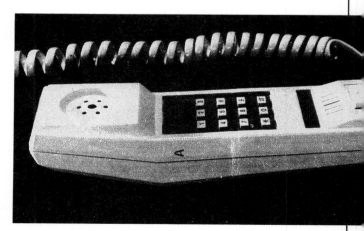

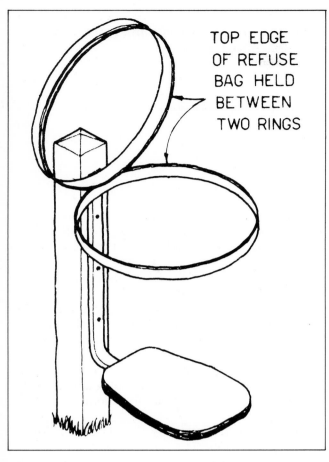

TOP EDGE
OF REFUSE
BAG HELD
BETWEEN
TWO RINGS

32 A litter container is shown in the sketch. The container consists of a frame which is attached to a wall or a post, and into which fits a plastics refuse bag. The platform at the base, supports the bag when it is full.

Orthographic views of the container are also given.

The company making the container decide that, with some modification it can be used in a garden for the collection of grass cuttings or leaves, although for this purpose it will need to be fitted with wheels and a handle.

a Produce design sketches of modifications to the container which will satisfy the design requirements;

b Draw **scale 1:5**, suitable orthographic views showing your design of the modified container;

c **Sketch freehand** a view of a wheel and part of the axle and underframe showing how the parts are assembled.

Dimensions not shown are left to your discretion.

Do not draw the refuse bag.

Do not shade or colour your drawings.

In sectional views, the sides of the tubes may be shown as thick lines. *(56 marks)* (WJEC)

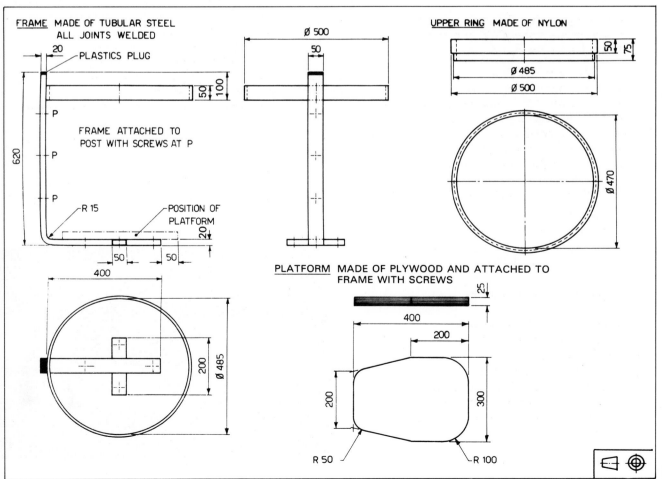

FRAME MADE OF TUBULAR STEEL ALL JOINTS WELDED

UPPER RING MADE OF NYLON

PLASTICS PLUG

FRAME ATTACHED TO POST WITH SCREWS AT P

R 15 — POSITION OF PLATFORM

PLATFORM MADE OF PLYWOOD AND ATTACHED TO FRAME WITH SCREWS

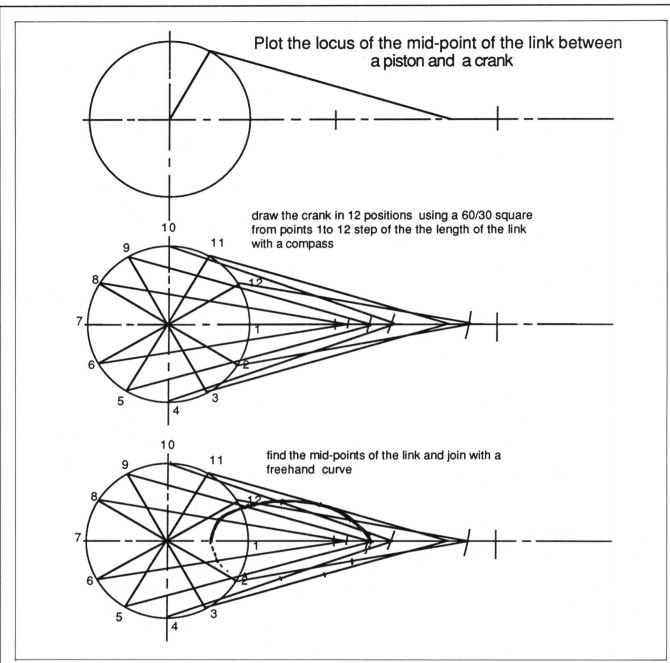

Plot the locus of the mid-point of the link between a piston and a crank

draw the crank in 12 positions using a 60/30 square
from points 1to 12 step of the the length of the link
with a compass

find the mid-points of the link and join with a
freehand curve

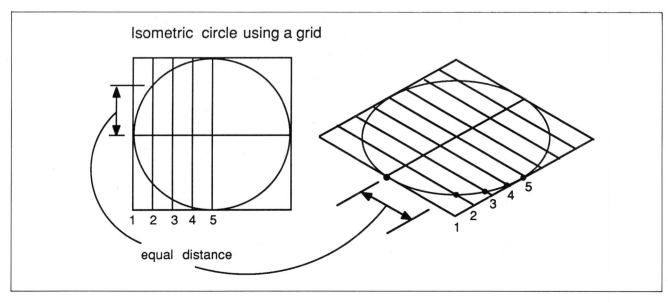

Isometric circle using a grid

equal distance

Tangential arcs

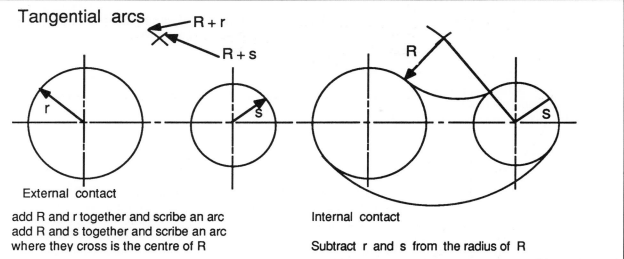

External contact

add R and r together and scribe an arc
add R and s together and scribe an arc
where they cross is the centre of R

Internal contact

Subtract r and s from the radius of R

Regular Polygons

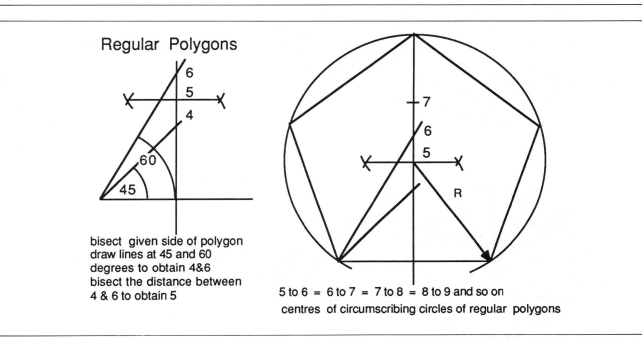

bisect given side of polygon
draw lines at 45 and 60
degrees to obtain 4&6
bisect the distance between
4 & 6 to obtain 5

5 to 6 = 6 to 7 = 7 to 8 = 8 to 9 and so on
centres of circumscribing circles of regular polygons

Ellipse given the major and minor axis

draw circles having diameter equal to the
lengths of the axis
draw a series of radial lines
draw verticals and horizontals as shown
the ellipse passes through the points of
intersection

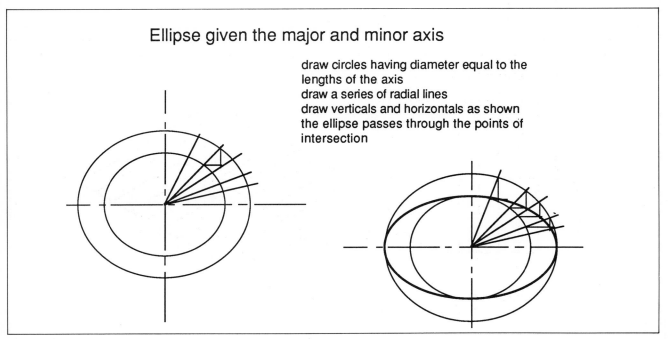

Materials

Craft, design and technology is a subject which requires considerable resources. Design and communication is no exception. The first book in this series, *Introducing Design and Communication*, gave a great deal of information on the range of media required for the subject; pencils, pens, markers and instruments, as well as the various types of papers and cards.

As you become more involved in the subject you will start to build up your own kit of equipment, including the make of fine line pen which gives you the best result, a range of colour pencils which you find most useful and a particular marker bought for a special presentation drawing. Make sure you look after your kit. Mark each item and find a box in which to keep them. My first container was a shoe box which I used whilst at school. I then progressed to a biscuit tin, next a fishing tackle box and only recently invested in a large cantilever artbin. Your container will need to grow as the range of your equipment builds up. I am still using pencils I bought whilst at school – it pays to look after your favourite tools.

Design and communication will also involve you in three-dimensional modelling as well as two-dimensional artwork. As you are aware, modelling requires a wide range of varied materials, but often only in small amounts. Always save scrap pieces of polystyrene, acrylic and balsa as well as more specialized items such as tapes and lettering. You never know when something will come in useful. These materials are also expensive, so you cannot afford to waste them.

You will no doubt have discovered a good supplier of graphics materials in your area. Always ask your teacher which shops to go to as it is likely that a reduction can be obtained on most things through educational suppliers. Your teacher will have a range of catalogues from which you will be able to select things. Three companies whose catalogues are worth consulting are:

Design Craft and Graphics
Ball Lane
Tackley
Oxford OX5 3AG
Tel. 0869 83611

C W Edding (UK) Ltd
North Orbital Estate
Napsbury Lane
St Albans
Herts AL1 1XQ
Tel. 0727 34471

Esmond Hellerman
Harris Way
Sunbury-on-Thames
Middx
Tel. 0932 81888

Most towns also have a specialized model making shop for railway and kit modelling. They usually stock a range of useful materials such as solvents, textures etc. A specialized model making supplier is Engineering Model Associates. They have a catalogue specifically for CDT which lists everything you could possibly require. Ask your teacher to show it to you, it is full of ideas.

EMA Model Supplies Ltd (CDT catalogue)
58–60 The Centre
Feltham
Middx
Tel. 01 890 5270/8404   01 751 2165

Publications

Although this book attempts to cover a great deal of the information you will need, other books will have to be consulted for more specific information. The books suggested here may be available at school. If not, try your public library.

Design history

The Conran Directory of Design (Ed. S. Bayley),
Octopus 1 85029 005 9
Design Source Book by P. Sparke, Macdonald
0 356 12005 8

Communication skills and techniques

Manual of Graphic Techniques Volumes 1, 2, 3 and 4
by P. Porter and B. Greenstreet, Astragal
0 906525 179+
Presentation Techniques by D. Powell, Orbis
0 85613 600
The Usborne Book of Graphic Design by S. Potter and
T. Peach, Usborne 0 7460 0092 8
Paper Engineering by M. Hinter, Tarquin
0 906212 49 9

Project books

GCSE Craft Design and Technology (Ed. R. Kimbell)
Thames/Hutchinson 0 09 172461 9
Craft Design and Technology: Projects for GCSE by
P. Shipley and K. Webster, Heinemann 0 435 759507

Reference books

*Graphical Symbols for Use in Schools and Colleges
PP 7307*: 1986
*Engineering and Drawing Practice for Schools and
Colleges PP 7308*: 1986
*Compendium of British Standards for Design and
Technology in Schools PD 7302*: 1983
Published by British Standards Institute,
Education Section
2 Park Street
London W1A 2BS

Magazines

Magazines are the best way of finding out what is
currently happening in the world of design. The
following are all of interest although some are rather
specialized:
Design – The Design Council (monthly)
Blueprint – Architecture and Design (bi-monthly)
Creative Review – Advertising and Graphics (monthly)
Graphics World – Graphics (bi-monthly)
Designer – Chartered Society of Designers
(bi-monthly)
Which? – The Consumers' Association (quarterly)

Computer software

The computer software you will have access to will
depend on the hardware available. The majority of
schools have either BBC or RML Nimbus systems,
although you might come across Amstrad,
Commodore, Atari or Apple, for example. Nearly all
micros have graphic potential and you will become
familiar with the appropriate software. Software used
in the production of this book was:

BBC Compatible	**Apple Macintosh**
AMX SuperArt	MacPaint, MacDraw, MacDraft
TechSoft Designer	Easy 3D
	Cricket Draw

INDEX